Grade 4

Unit Resource Guide
Unit 12
Exploring Fractions

SECOND EDITION

A Mathematical Journey Using Science and Language Arts

KENDALL/HUNT PUBLISHING COMPANY
4050 Westmark Drive Dubuque, Iowa 52002

A TIMS® Curriculum
University of Illinois at Chicago

UIC The University of Illinois at Chicago

The original edition was based on work supported by the National Science Foundation under grant No. MDR 9050226 and the University of Illinois at Chicago. Any opinions, findings, and conclusions or recommendations expressed in this publication are those of the author(s) and do not necessarily reflect the views of the granting agencies.

ISBN 0-7872-8605-2

Printed in the United States of America

1 2 3 4 5 6 7 8 9 10 07 06 05 04 03

LETTER HOME

Exploring Fractions

Date: ______________________

Dear Family Member:

The activities in this unit will help your child better understand fractions. In this unit, your child will explore the concept of a whole. Understanding the size of the whole is important to understanding the fractional parts of that whole. For example, a half gallon of milk is larger than a half cup of milk because the whole is larger.

Another important idea is shown in the picture. The fewer pieces the pie is divided into, the larger each piece will be. Grace ate more pie than Shannon—$\frac{2}{4}$ is greater than $\frac{2}{12}$. Your child will use concrete models to name fractions, compare the size of fractions, and add and subtract fractions.

Shannon ate $\frac{2}{12}$ of an apple pie, Jessie ate $\frac{2}{6}$ of a peach pie, and Grace ate $\frac{2}{4}$ of a cherry pie. Who ate the most pie?

You can help your child understand fractions by pointing out places where fractions are used outside of school. Examples include preparing a recipe, measuring wood for a project, purchasing fabric, or advertising sales.

Continue the ongoing practice of the division facts. In this unit, students will practice and then take a quiz on the division facts for the nines. Use the *Triangle Flash Cards: 9s* to help your child practice these facts.

Thank you for your time and cooperation.

Sincerely,

____

UNIT 12

UNIT OUTLINE

Estimated Class Sessions
12–16

Exploring Fractions

Pacing Suggestions

- Lesson 4 *Frabble Game and Bubble Sort* is an optional lesson. These activities provide opportunities to practice and extend fraction concepts in game situations.
- Lesson 6 *Pattern Block Fractions* contains an optional activity from third grade that introduces students to using pattern blocks to represent fractions. Use it with those students who have not had these experiences.

Components Key: SG = Student Guide, DAB = Discovery Assignment Book, AB = Adventure Book, URG = Unit Resource Guide, and DPP = Daily Practice and Problems

	Sessions	Description	Supplies
LESSON 1 **Fraction Strips** **SG** pages 326–332 **DAB** pages 199–201 **URG** pages 24–38 **DPP** A–F	3	**ACTIVITY:** Students fold uniform strips of paper to show equal parts, labeling each part according to the fractional part it represents. Students will fold halves, thirds, fourths, fifths, sixths, eighths, ninths, tenths, and twelfths. Students will then use the strips to find equivalent fractions.	• scissors • envelopes • crayons, markers, or colored pencils • rulers
LESSON 2 **Adding and Subtracting with Fraction Strips** **SG** pages 333–335 **URG** pages 39–43 **DPP** G–H	1	**ACTIVITY:** Students use fraction strips to add and subtract fractions with like denominators.	
LESSON 3 **Comparing Fractions** **SG** pages 336–338 **URG** pages 44–50 **DPP** I–J	1	**ACTIVITY:** Students organize their fraction strips in a chart and then use the chart to compare and order fractions according to size.	• glue • blank paper

	Sessions	Description	Supplies
LESSON 4		– OPTIONAL LESSON –	
Frabble Game and Bubble Sort SG pages 339–342 DAB pages 203–209 URG pages 51–56	1–2	**OPTIONAL GAME:** Students use a deck of fraction cards to complete two activities. First, students play a game in small groups in which they order fractions according to size by strategically placing cards on the table. Then, in an activity called *Bubble Sort,* each student holds a fraction card as he or she stands in line. Following simple rules, they rearrange themselves so that the cards are in order.	• scissors
LESSON 5			
Equivalent Fractions SG pages 343–345 URG pages 57–64 DPP K–L	1	**ACTIVITY:** Students find equivalent fractions using their fraction charts from Lesson 3, write number sentences to represent the fractions, and look for patterns in the number sentences. They use the patterns to write an equivalent fraction for a given fraction.	
LESSON 6			
Pattern Block Fractions SG pages 346–349 URG pages 65–76 DPP M–P	2–3	**ACTIVITY:** Students explore the use of pattern blocks to model fractions. They name fractions when a given pattern block is defined as one whole, and they identify the whole when a fraction is given. They also model easy addition problems using pattern blocks.	• pattern blocks
LESSON 7			
Solving Problems with Pattern Blocks SG pages 350–352 URG pages 77–82 DPP Q–R	1	**ACTIVITY:** Students use pattern blocks to order fractions by looking at patterns. They develop a strategy for ordering fractions. They also solve word problems involving addition of fractions using pattern blocks.	• pattern blocks
LESSON 8			
Fraction Puzzles SG pages 353–355 URG pages 83–93 DPP S–V	2	**ASSESSMENT ACTIVITY:** Students work cooperatively in groups of four to solve fraction puzzles. Four clues are given to help the groups solve each puzzle. After finding a solution, students write a paragraph explaining their solutions and the problem-solving strategies used by their groups. **ASSESSMENT PAGE:** *Puzzle Problem,* Unit Resource Guide, page 92.	• pattern blocks

LESSON 9	Sessions	Description	Supplies
Midterm Test URG pages 94–101 DPP W–X	1–2	**ASSESSMENT ACTIVITY:** Students take a test on concepts in this and past units. **ASSESSMENT PAGES:** *Midterm Test,* Unit Resource Guide, pages 96–100.	• calculators • rulers • protractors • base-ten pieces • pattern blocks

CONNECTIONS

A current list of connections is available at www.mathtrailblazers.com.

Software

Suggested Titles

- *Fraction Attraction* develops understanding of fractions using fraction bars, pie charts, hundreds blocks, and other materials.
- *Fraction Operation* develops conceptual understanding of fraction operations.
- *Math Arena* is a collection of math activities that reinforces many math concepts.
- *Math Munchers Deluxe* provides practice with equivalent fractions and other skills in an arcade-like game.
- *Math Mysteries Fractions* develops multistep problem solving with fractions.
- *Math Workshop Deluxe* allows students to explore fractions and decimals.
- *Mighty Math Number Heroes* poses short answer questions about fractions and other number operations.
- *National Library of Virtual Manipulatives* website (http://matti.usu.edu) allows students to work with fractions using pattern blocks and other manipulatives on the computer.
- *Representing Fractions* provides a conceptual introduction to fractions.

UNIT 12 BACKGROUND

Exploring Fractions

Throughout the *Math Trailblazers*™ curriculum, students have used manipulatives to explore fractions. In this unit, students will continue to build a strong conceptual understanding of fractions through the use of manipulatives.

Most fractions that we encounter fall into one of the following contexts:

- part-whole fractions
- indicated divisions
- ratios
- measurements
- names of points on a number line
- pure numbers
- probabilities

In this unit, part-whole fractions are the main focus. However, fractions of measurements are also included. Other units within the curriculum will focus on other types of fractions.

Learning about fractions is often a difficult task for children. This difficulty is understandable considering the complexity of the concepts involved. The fact that many children misunderstand fractions is illustrated by the results of the National Assessment of Educational Progress (Kouba, et al., 1988). In this assessment, many 9-, 13-, and 17-year-olds were shown to lack proficiency in working with fractions. Students appeared to have done their computations mechanically with little understanding of the underlying fraction concepts (National Research Council, 2001).

When students begin to study fractions, they usually have a good understanding of the system of whole numbers. Unless students develop a conceptual understanding of fractions, this understanding of whole number concepts often interferes with their abilities to learn fraction concepts. The following represent some of the roadblocks students may experience if conceptual understanding of fractions is not developed.

1. Consider the symbol $\frac{3}{4}$. This number is made up of two parts, the numerator and the denominator, each represented by a whole number with a specific meaning or value. The denominator tells us that the whole is divided into 4 equal parts, and the numerator tells us that we are concerned with 3 of these parts. In addition to understanding these two values, a student must understand that the symbol $\frac{3}{4}$ also represents a single number with a unique value.
2. Students learn in the whole number system that 4 is less than 6. However, when comparing the fractions $\frac{1}{4}$ and $\frac{1}{6}$, $\frac{1}{4}$ is larger than $\frac{1}{6}$. Students may have difficulty with the inverse relationship between the number of parts into which the whole is divided and the size of these parts. That is, the more parts a whole is divided into, the smaller each part is. The following exchange between a teacher and student illustrates this confusion (Post, et al., 1985):

Teacher: One-fifth and one-ninth—which is less?

Student: One-fifth is less, because five is less than nine.

[The teacher directs the student to use colored parts to illustrate.]

Student: [Covers one circular unit with orange ($\frac{1}{5}$) parts and another with white ($\frac{1}{9}$) parts, as shown in Figure 1.] It takes 9 white and 5 orange.

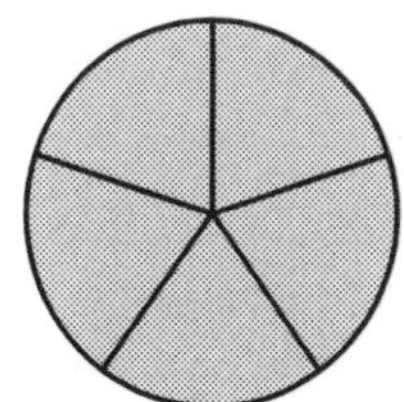

Figure 1: *Two fraction circles illustrating fifths and ninths*

Teacher: [Draws attention to colored parts] Which is less, one-fifth or one-ninth?

Student: One-fifth, because it takes five to cover this, and it takes nine to cover this [points to the circular units].

Student: One orange is bigger than one white. One-fifth is less than one-ninth.

3. The previous vignette also illustrates the difficulty many students have with the language we use in the classroom as we teach fractions. This language may not be clearly understood by all students. For example when we ask, "Which fraction is less?" do we mean which is less in size or do we mean which needs a lesser amount to cover the whole? Likewise, when asking, "Which is greater?" are we asking which fraction covers a greater area of the whole or which fraction results in a greater number of parts?
4. As students begin to compare and order fractions, their understanding of the whole number system is further challenged. When students order fractions with like denominators, they use the numerators to order the fractions. Ordering fractions using the numerator has a direct relationship to the whole number system. That is, $\frac{1}{4} < \frac{2}{4} < \frac{3}{4} < \frac{4}{4}$. However, when students compare and order fractions with like numerators, this relationship changes. Students use the denominators to order fractions, finding that $\frac{2}{9} < \frac{2}{5} < \frac{2}{3}$. When both the numerators and denominators are different, students must have a solid understanding of fractions so that they can choose efficient and flexible strategies to compare the fractions.
5. Students can also become confused with counting issues when working with fractions. For example, when you count using whole numbers, you know that 1 comes before 2 and 3 comes after 2. However, when counting with fractions it is difficult to know what comes next. For example, what fraction follows $\frac{1}{2}$ on the number line?

Each of these roadblocks can affect a child's understanding of fractions and subsequent ability to use them correctly. Students need experiences in the classroom that will help them develop a strong conceptual understanding of fractions. The use of manipulatives is crucial in developing this understanding. Research has shown that students who learn with the help of manipulatives generally scored higher on achievement tests than students whose instruction included no use of manipulatives. (Suydam, 1986) There should be an emphasis on the use of manipulatives in the classroom to help students construct fraction meaning as they explore fraction concepts. Furthermore, students should use more than one type of manipulative as they explore fractions. This increases the likelihood that students will generalize their understandings beyond the tangible (the manipulatives) to the symbolic representation. In this unit, both paper folding and pattern blocks are used to help students develop a strong mental image of fractions. Students use both these physical models to name fractions and to represent fractions when given a fraction value.

The concept of a unit or a whole is explored using pattern blocks. Students are asked to find the value of different blocks based on the defined whole. For example, when a yellow hexagon is defined as one whole, the blue rhombus equals $\frac{1}{3}$ of the whole. However, when a red trapezoid is defined as one whole, the green triangle equals $\frac{1}{3}$. Students develop the understanding that the size of the fraction depends on the size of the whole.

Students explore equivalent fractions using both paper folding and pattern blocks. Students also compare fractions using both manipulatives. Comparisons of fractions with like denominators and like numerators are explored. Students are encouraged to develop a strategy for ordering fractions with like numerators.

Finally, students are introduced to simple addition and subtraction of fractions using manipulatives. Students are introduced to the symbolic representation of these problems. However, they are only expected to solve problems in which the symbolic representations are paired with physical models.

Resources

- Cramer, K., T. Post, and R. del Mas. "Initial Fraction Learning by Fourth- and Fifth-Grade Students: A Comparison of the Effects of Using Commercial Curricula with the Effects of Using the Rational Number Project Curriculum." *Journal for Research in Mathematics Education,* 33(2), pp. 111–144, March 2002.
- Curcio, Frances R. (series editor). *Curriculum and Evaluation Standards for School Mathematics, Addenda Series 5–8: Understanding Rational Numbers and Proportions.* National Council of Teachers of Mathematics, Reston, VA, 1994.
- Driscoll, Mark J. *Research Within Reach, Elementary School Mathematics.* National Council of Teachers of Mathematics, Reston, VA, 1986.
- Kouba, et al. "Result of the Fourth NAEP Assessment of Mathematics: Number, Operations, and Word Problems." *Arithmetic Teacher,* 35 (8), April 1988.
- National Research Council. *Adding It Up: Helping Children Learn Mathematics.* J. Kilpatrick, J. Swafford, and B. Findell, Eds. Mathematics Learning Study Committee, Center for Education, Division of Behavioral and Social Sciences and Education, National Academy Press, Washington, DC, 2001.
- Post, Thomas, Ipke Wachsmuth, Richard Lesh, Merlyn Behr. "Order and Equivalence of Rational Numbers: A Cognitive Analysis." *Journal for Research in Mathematics Education,* 16 (1), January 1985.
- Post, Thomas R. (editor). *Teaching Mathematics in Grades K–8, Research Based Methods.* Allyn and Bacon, Boston, 1992.
- Suydam, Marilyn. "Manipulatives, Materials and Achievement." *Arithmetic Teacher,* 33 (6), February 1986.
- Trafton, Paul, and Albert P. Shulte, (editors). *New Directions for Elementary School Mathematics, 1989 Yearbook.* National Council of Teachers of Mathematics, Reston, VA, 1989.

Assessment Indicators

- Can students represent fractions using pattern blocks and paper folding?
- Can students identify the whole when given a fractional part of the whole?
- Can students find equivalent fractions using manipulatives?
- Can students compare and order fractions using manipulatives?
- Can students add and subtract fractions with like denominators using manipulatives?
- Can students solve open-response problems and communicate solution strategies?
- Do students demonstrate fluency with the division facts for the 9s?

OBSERVATIONAL ASSESSMENT RECORD

- **A1** Can students represent fractions using pattern blocks and paper folding?
- **A2** Can students identify the whole when given a fractional part of the whole?
- **A3** Can students find equivalent fractions using manipulatives?
- **A4** Can students compare and order fractions using manipulatives?
- **A5** Can students add and subtract fractions with like denominators using manipulatives?
- **A6** Can students solve open-response problems and communicate solution strategies?
- **A7** Do students demonstrate fluency with the division facts for the 9s?
- **A8** ____________________

Name	A1	A2	A3	A4	A5	A6	A7	A8	Comments
1.									
2.									
3.									
4.									
5.									
6.									
7.									
8.									
9.									
10.									
11.									
12.									
13.									

Name	A1	A2	A3	A4	A5	A6	A7	A8	Comments
14.									
15.									
16.									
17.									
18.									
19.									
20.									
21.									
22.									
23.									
24.									
25.									
26.									
27.									
28.									
29.									
30.									
31.									
32.									

Daily Practice and Problems

Exploring Fractions

Two Daily Practice and Problems (DPP) items are included for each class session listed in the Unit Outline. The first item is always a Bit and the second is either a Task or a Challenge. Refer to the Daily Practice and Problems and Home Practice Guide in the *Teacher Implementation Guide* for further information on the DPP. A Scope and Sequence Chart for the Daily Practice and Problems for the year can be found in the Scope and Sequence Chart & the NCTM *Principles and Standards* section of the *Teacher Implementation Guide.*

A DPP Menu for Unit 12

Eight icons designate the subject matter of the Daily Practice and Problems (DPP) items. Each DPP item falls into one or more of the categories listed below. A brief menu of the DPP items included in Unit 12 follows.

Number Sense	Computation	Time	Geometry
E, H–J, O, Q–V	D, J–L, P	A, F	N, X
Math Facts	**Money**	**Measurement**	**Data**
B, C, G, H, K–M, P, W	F, V	N, X	

Practice and Assessment of the Division Facts

The DPP for this unit continues the systematic strategies-based approach to learning the division facts. This unit provides practice and assessment for the nines. The *Triangle Flash Cards: 9s* may be found in the *Discovery Assignment Book* following the Home Practice and in the *Grade 4 Facts Resource Guide*. A discussion of the flash cards and how they might be used can be found in item B of the DPP. A quiz on these facts is provided in item W.

For more information about the distribution and assessment of the math facts, see the TIMS Tutor: *Math Facts* in the *Teacher Implementation Guide* and the *Grade 4 Facts Resource Guide*. Also refer to the DPP guides in the *Unit Resource Guide* for Units 3 and 9.

Daily Practice and Problems

Students may solve the items individually, in groups, or as a class. The items may also be assigned for homework.

Student Questions	Teacher Notes
A Telling Time How much time has passed from: A. 12:10 to 12:30? B. 1:45 to 2:05? C. 3:20 to 4:00? D. 5:25 to 5:55? E. 11:10 to 12:25?	**TIMS Bit** A. 20 minutes B. 20 minutes C. 40 minutes D. 30 minutes E. 1 hour and 15 minutes

Student Questions	Teacher Notes
 **Division Facts: 9s** With a partner, use your *Triangle Flash Cards: 9s* to quiz each other on the division facts for the nines. Ask your partner first to cover the numbers in the squares. Use the two uncovered numbers to solve a division fact. Separate the flash cards into three piles: those facts you know and can answer quickly, those that you can figure out with a strategy, and those that you need to learn. Then, go through the cards again and have your partner cover the numbers in the circles. Use the uncovered numbers to solve a division fact. Separate the cards into three piles again. Both times through, practice the facts that are in the last two piles and make a list of these facts so that you can practice them at home. Circle all the facts you know and can answer quickly on your *Division Facts I Know* chart. Repeat this process for your partner.	**TIMS Task**  The *Triangle Flash Cards: 9s* are located after the Home Practice in the *Discovery Assignment Book*. Blackline masters of all the flash cards, organized by group, are in the Generic Section and in the *Grade 4 Facts Resource Guide*. Part 1 of the Home Practice reminds students to take home the list of facts they need to study as well as their flash cards. Inform students when the quiz on the nines will be given. This quiz appears in TIMS Bit W.

Student Questions	Teacher Notes

C Division Facts

A. 81 ÷ 9 =

B. 9 ÷ 9 =

C. 63 ÷ 9 =

D. 27 ÷ 9 =

E. 36 ÷ 9 =

F. 54 ÷ 9 =

G. 18 ÷ 9 =

H. 72 ÷ 9 =

I. 9 ÷ 1 =

J. 45 ÷ 9 =

TIMS Bit

A. 9 B. 1

C 7 D. 3

E. 4 F. 6

G. 2 H. 8

I. 9 J. 5

D Multiplication

Use paper and pencil or mental math to solve the following problems. Estimate to make sure your answers are reasonable.

1. A. 53 × 4 = B. 459 × 4 =

   C. 5532 × 4 = D. 26 × 45 =

   E. 22 × 7 = F. 724 × 3 =

   G. 3096 × 5 = H. 38 × 52 =

2. Explain your strategy for Question 1A.

3. Explain your estimation strategy for Question 1D.

TIMS Task

1. A. 212 B. 1836

   C. 22,128 D. 1170

   E. 154 F. 2172

   G. 15,480 H. 1976

2. Possible mental math strategy:
   4 × 50 = 200;
   4 × 3 = 12;
   200 + 12 = 212.

3. Possible strategy:
   Round 26 up to 30;
   round 45 down to 40;
   30 × 40 = 1200.

E Decimals in Sequence

Write the next 3 decimals:

A. 1.0 1.5 2.0 2.5 3.0 __ __ __

B. 6.4 6.8 7.2 7.6 8.0 __ __ __

C. 2.2 3.2 4.2 5.2 6.2 __ __ __

TIMS Bit

A. 3.5, 4.0, 4.5

B. 8.4, 8.8, 9.2

C. 7.2, 8.2, 9.2

Student Questions	Teacher Notes

Earning an Allowance

Irma's aunt pays her 5 cents each minute she reads a book instead of watching television. She began reading at 4:48 and finished at 5:19. How much money did she make? Tell the strategies you used to get your answer.

TIMS Task

$1.55

More Division Facts

Find the number *n* that makes the sentence true.

A. $72 \div 8 = n$ B. $n \div 9 = 6$

C. $n \div 9 = 5$ D. $36 \div 4 = n$

E. $27 \div n = 9$ F. $n \div 9 = 9$

G. $n \div 9 = 2$ H. $63 \div n = 9$

TIMS Bit 

A. 9 **B.** 54

C 45 **D.** 9

E. 3 **F.** 81

G. 18 **H.** 7

Prime Factors

1. Which of the following are prime numbers?

   53 54 57 67 96 103

2. For the composite numbers, use factor trees to factor them into a product of primes. You may use a calculator to help.

TIMS Task 

1. 53, 67, 103

2.

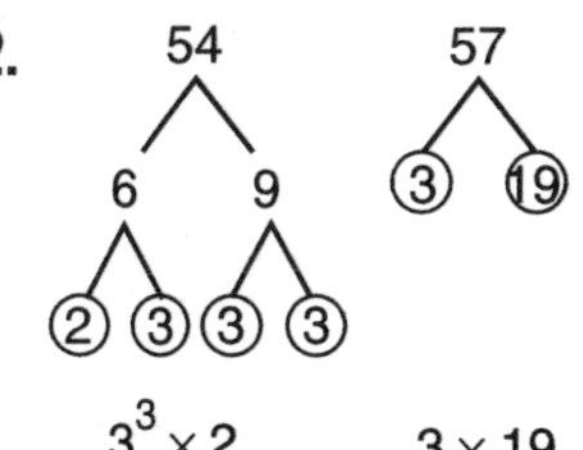

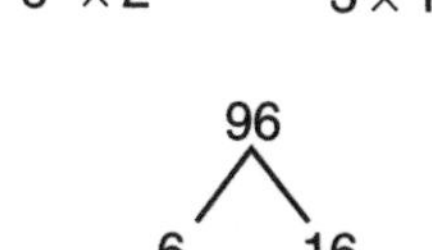

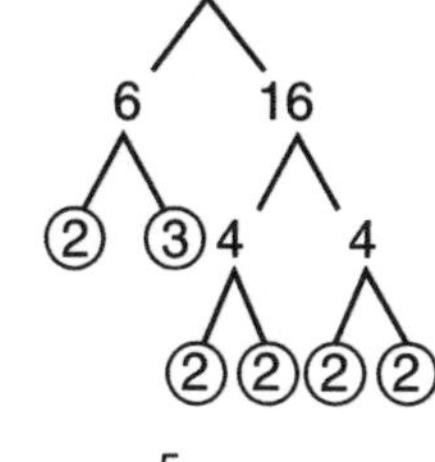

Student Questions	Teacher Notes

Decimals from Pictures

Write a decimal for the shaded part of each picture. The flat is one whole.

1. 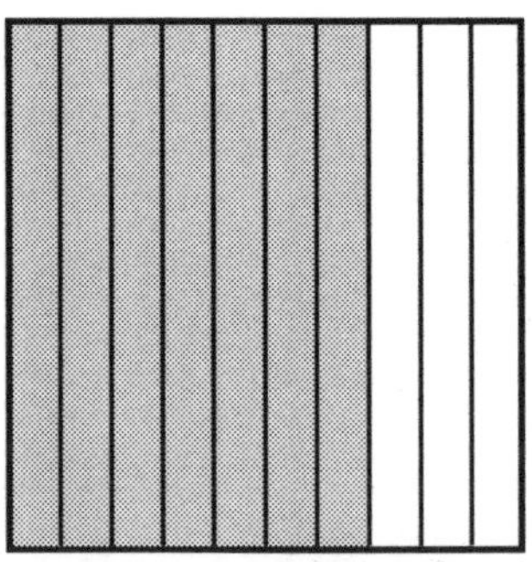

2. 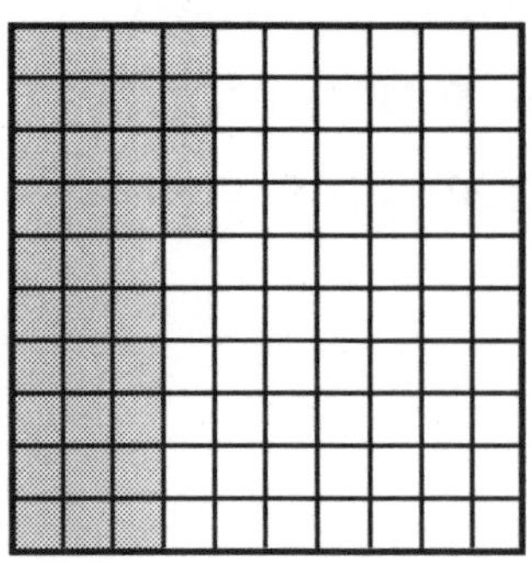

3. 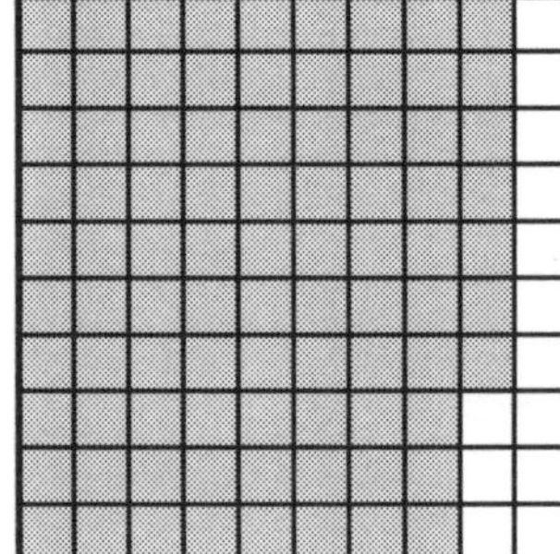

4. 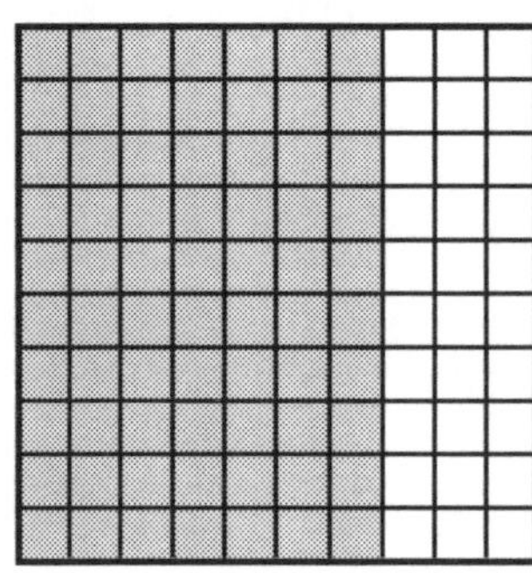

TIMS Bit

1. 0.7
2. 0.34
3. 0.87
4. 0.70 or 0.7

J More Multiplication

1. Solve the following using a paper-and-pencil method.

   A. $239 \times 7 =$ B. $3729 \times 3 =$

   C. $2390 \times 2 =$ D. $79 \times 23 =$

2. Find at least two ways to round each of the answers to Questions 1A through 1D.

TIMS Task

1. A. 1673
   B. 11,187
   C. 4780
   D. 1817

Answers will vary for Question 2. Possible answers are given below.

2. A. 2000; 1700; 1500
   B. 11,000; 11,200
   C. 5000; 4800
   D. 2000; 1800

Student Questions	Teacher Notes
 **More Division Fact Practice** Find the number n that makes each sentence true. A. $54 \div n = 9$ B. $720 \div n = 90$ C. $n \times 400 = 36,000$ D. $70 \times n = 63,000$ E. $90 \times n = 450$ F. $n \div 9 = 300$	**TIMS Bit**   A. 6 B. 8 C 90 D. 900 E. 5 F. 2700
L Fact Practice A. $30 \times 90 =$ B. $630 \div 70 =$ C. $360 \div 9 =$ D. $90 \times 80 =$ E. $2700 \div 9 =$ F. $9000 \times 90 =$ G. $54,000 \div 9 =$ H. $1800 \div 90 =$ I. $900 \times 0 =$ J. $900 \div 90 =$	**TIMS Task**   A. 2700 B. 9 C 40 D. 7200 E. 300 F. 810,000 G. 6000 H. 20 I. 0 J. 10

Student Questions	Teacher Notes

Fact Families for × and ÷

Solve the given fact. Then, name another fact that is in the same fact family.

A. $9 \times 8 =$

B. $54 \div 9 =$

C. $36 \div 4 =$

D. $9 \times 7 =$

TIMS Bit

Complete this item orally as a class. One student can solve the given fact and another student can name a related fact. The answers and possible related facts are:

A. 72; $72 \div 9 = 8$

B. 6; $6 \times 9 = 54$

C. 9; $4 \times 9 = 36$

D. 63; $63 \div 7 = 9$

N Area

1. Draw two different shapes on *Centimeter Grid Paper.* Each shape should have an area of 21.5 square centimeters.
2. Measure the perimeter of your two shapes to the nearest tenth of a centimeter. Are the perimeters the same or different?

TIMS Challenge

1. Two sample shapes are shown below.

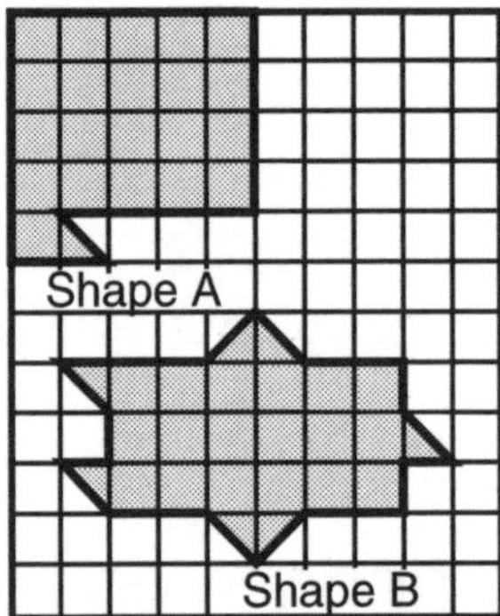

2. Perimeter of Shape A is 21.4 cm. Perimeter of Shape B is 23.8 cm. Be aware that lines on the diagonal are longer than 1 cm.

Student Questions	Teacher Notes

 Evenly Divisible

Frank wants to buy stickers for his 6 friends who will be attending his birthday party. At the store, he sees four different collections of stickers.

One pad has 95 stickers.
One pad has 110 stickers.
One pad has 120 stickers.
One pad has 160 stickers.

Frank plans to buy one pad of stickers. If he wants to divide the stickers evenly among his 6 guests without any leftovers, which pad should he purchase? How did you decide?

TIMS Bit 

120 is divisible by 2 (it is even) and by 3 (the sum of the digits in 120 is a multiple of 3). Since 120 is divisible by 2 and 3, it is divisible by 6. Encourage students to share their strategies. Calculators should be available.

 Division Stories

Write a division story for $28 \div 9$. Draw a picture for your story and write a number sentence that describes it. In your story, explain any remainder.

TIMS Task  

Stories and pictures will vary. Students should label their pictures with the number sentence.

$28 \div 9 = 3$ R1 or
$3 \times 9 + 1 = 28$

 Confused!

On planet Zimbo, a Zimbonese was told that the number 6 was larger than the number 4. But now there is confusion because the Zimbonese has also been told that $\frac{1}{6}$ is smaller than $\frac{1}{4}$. Please use a diagram to explain why $\frac{1}{6}$ is smaller than $\frac{1}{4}$.

TIMS Bit 

Possible diagram:

$\frac{1}{4}$			

$\frac{1}{6}$					

It's important that the whole be the same for both fractions so that when divided into six pieces, a one-sixth piece will be smaller than a piece from a whole divided into four pieces.

Student Questions	Teacher Notes

R Further Confusion

Brandon and Lee Yah invited the Zimbonese to eat pizza with them. Brandon has $\frac{1}{8}$ of a pizza and it is bigger in size than Lee Yah's $\frac{1}{4}$ of a pizza. The Zimbonese thought it understood (see DPP Bit Q) that $\frac{1}{8}$ was smaller than $\frac{1}{4}$. What needs to be changed so that $\frac{1}{8}$ is less than $\frac{1}{4}$?

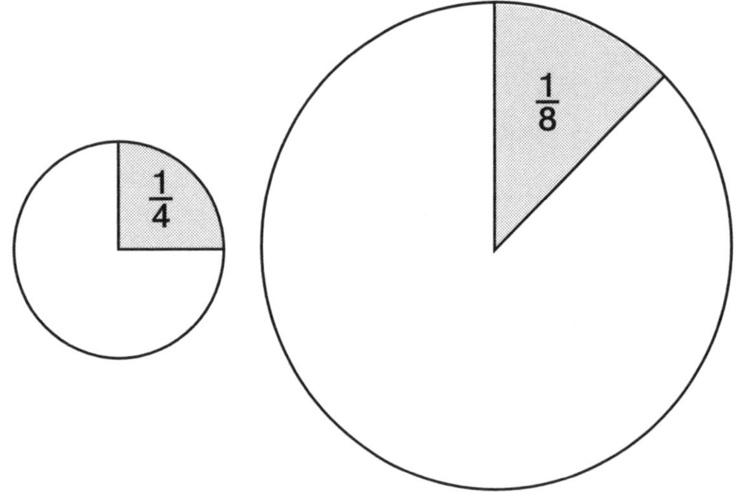

TIMS Task N

The pizzas need to be the same size. Encourage students to write in their journals what they've learned from the previous Bit and this Task.

S Words to Numbers

1. Write the following words as numbers.

   A. two-thirds B. six-tenths

   C. five-eighths D. one-twelfth

2. Write the following numbers as words.

   A. $\frac{3}{4}$ B. $\frac{7}{9}$

   C. $\frac{1}{2}$ D. $\frac{2}{5}$

TIMS Bit N

1. A. $\frac{2}{3}$

B. $\frac{6}{10}$ **or 0.6**

C. $\frac{5}{8}$

D. $\frac{1}{12}$

2. A. three-fourths

B. seven-ninths

C. one-half

D. two-fifths

Student Questions	Teacher Notes
 **Art Paper** Carlos and Brandon each cut out a rectangle from a piece of drawing paper. Carlos's rectangle was larger—it was $\frac{1}{2}$ of his piece of paper. Brandon's was smaller, but it was $\frac{3}{4}$ of his whole piece. 1. Use *Centimeter Grid Paper* to draw a sketch of Brandon's and Carlos's whole pieces of paper. 2. Shade $\frac{1}{2}$ of Carlos's piece of paper. 3. Shade $\frac{3}{4}$ of Brandon's piece of paper.	**TIMS Challenge** N **Accept all correct diagrams.** 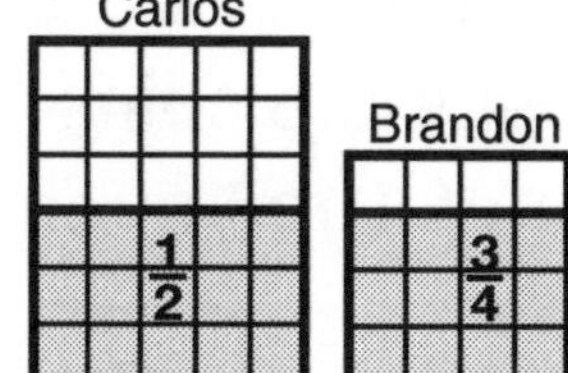
 **Even Products** In your journal, explain why all the multiples of 4 are even numbers. First, write all the multiples in order from 4 to 40.	**TIMS Bit**  **4, 8, 12, 16, 20, 24, 28, 32, 36, 40** **The multiples of 4 are even because a number divisible by 4 is also divisible by 2. Two is a factor of 4. All multiples of 2 are even.**

Bank Deposit

The bank gives Maya wrappers so she can roll the coins she saves. Then, she deposits the coins. The table shows the value of 1 roll of each type of coin.

Type of Coin	Value of 1 Roll
pennies	50¢
nickels	$2.00
dimes	$5.00
quarters	$10.00

Maya counts her change and puts the coins in wrappers. She has a total of $18.68. What types of coins could she have? How many full rolls of these coins could she have? How many coins would she have left over? List two possible combinations.

TIMS Challenge N $

Accept all possible answers. Two examples are listed below.

1 roll of quarters ($10) + 1 roll of dimes ($5) + 1 roll of nickels ($2) + 3 rolls of pennies ($.50 + $.50 + $.50) = $18.50 with 18¢ left over

or

3 rolls of dimes ($5 + $5 + $5) + 1 roll of nickels ($2) + 3 rolls of pennies ($.50 + $.50 + $.50) = $18.50 with 18¢ left over.

18¢ left over (18 pennies; 1 dime and 8 pennies; 1 dime, 1 nickel, and 3 pennies; 2 nickels and 8 pennies; 3 nickels and 3 pennies)

Student Questions	Teacher Notes

Division Quiz: 9s

A. $72 \div 9 =$

B. $63 \div 9 =$

C. $54 \div 9 =$

D. $36 \div 9 =$

E. $81 \div 9 =$

F. $45 \div 9 =$

G. $9 \div 9 =$

H. $27 \div 9 =$

I. $18 \div 9 =$

TIMS Bit

A. 8 B. 7

C. 6 D. 4

E. 9 F. 5

G. 1 H. 3

I. 2

We recommend 1 minute for this quiz. Allow students to change pens after the time is up and complete the remaining problems in a different color. After students take the test, have them update their *Division Facts I Know* charts.

Since students learned the division facts through work with fact families, it is likely that the student who answers $72 \div 9$ correctly also knows the answer to $72 \div 8$. To make sure, however, after the quiz, ask students to write a related division fact for each of the facts on the quiz. A student who answers a given fact correctly and who also writes the correct related fact can circle both facts on the chart.

Drawing Line Segments

Draw a 5-cm segment on your paper and label the endpoints E and G. Measure and mark the midpoint with the letter F. Extend the line 2 cm past E and label the new endpoint D. Now measure the length of $\overline{DF}$.

TIMS Task

2 cm 2.5 cm 2.5 cm

D E F G

$\overline{DF}$ is 4.5 cm long.

Daily Practice and Problems: Bits for Lesson 1

A. Telling Time (URG p. 12)

How much time has passed from:

A. 12:10 to 12:30?

B. 1:45 to 2:05?

C. 3:20 to 4:00?

D. 5:25 to 5:55?

E. 11:10 to 12:25?

C. Division Facts (URG p. 14)

A. 81 ÷ 9 = B. 9 ÷ 9 =

C. 63 ÷ 9 = D. 27 ÷ 9 =

E. 36 ÷ 9 = F. 54 ÷ 9 =

G. 18 ÷ 9 = H. 72 ÷ 9 =

I. 9 ÷ 1 = J. 45 ÷ 9 =

E. Decimals in Sequence (URG p. 14)

Write the next 3 decimals:

A. 1.0 1.5 2.0 2.5 3.0 __ __ __

B. 6.4 6.8 7.2 7.6 8.0 __ __ __

C. 2.2 3.2 4.2 5.2 6.2 __ __ __

DPP Tasks are on page 33. Suggestions for using the DPPs are on page 33.

LESSON GUIDE

Fraction Strips

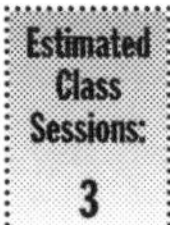

Estimated Class Sessions: 3

Students fold uniform strips of paper into equal parts, labeling each part according to the fraction it represents. Strips will be folded to show halves, thirds, fourths, fifths, sixths, eighths, ninths, tenths, and twelfths. Students will use their completed strips to show specific fractions and to name fractions. They will also use their strips to find and name equivalent fractions. The strips will also be used in Lessons 2–5.

Key Content

- Representing fractions using paper folding and symbols.
- Defining numerator and denominator.
- Identifying fractional parts of a whole.
- Comparing fractions using manipulatives.

Key Vocabulary

denominator
equivalent fraction
fraction
numerator

Curriculum Sequence

Before This Unit

In third grade, students explored fraction concepts in Units 13 and 17. They named fractions, found equivalent fractions, and compared fractions. In Unit 15, students investigated decimals and made connections between decimals and common fractions.

In fourth grade, students investigated decimal fractions in Unit 10.

After This Unit

Students will use fractions in their study of probability in Unit 14. They will learn paper-and-pencil methods for the operations of addition, subtraction, and multiplication of fractions in fifth grade. See Grade 5 Units 3, 5, 11, and 12.

Materials List

Print Materials for Students

		Math Facts and Daily Practice and Problems	Activity	Homework
Student Books	Student Guide		*Fraction Strips* Page 326	*Fraction Strips* Homework Section Pages 327–332
Student Books	Discovery Assignment Book		*Making Fraction Strips* Pages 199–201	Home Practice Parts 1 & 2 Page 193 and *Triangle Flash Cards: 9s* Page 197
Teacher Resources	Facts Resource Guide ◎	DPP Items 12B & 12C Use the *Triangle Flash Cards: 9s* to review the division facts for this group.		
Teacher Resources	Unit Resource Guide	DPP Items A–F Pages 12–15 ◎		

◎ *available on Teacher Resource CD*

All Transparency Masters, Blackline Masters, and Assessment Blackline Masters in the Unit Resource Guide are on the Teacher Resource CD.

Supplies for Each Student

scissors
2 envelopes (1 for storing flash cards and 1 for fraction strips)
crayons, markers, or colored pencils
ruler

Materials for the Teacher

Fraction Strips for the Teacher Blackline Masters (Unit Resource Guide) Pages 36–37
Observational Assessment Record (Unit Resource Guide, Pages 9–10 and Teacher Resource CD)

Before the Activity

Using the *Fraction Strips for the Teacher* Blackline Masters, cut out, color, and fold one set of fraction strips to be used as a class sample.

Students have worked with fraction concepts since first grade. They have used physical models to identify and compare fractions. This is the first concentrated study of common fractions in fourth grade, however. Before starting this lesson, assess students' prior knowledge about fractions. Draw a rectangle on the blackboard or on an overhead transparency. Tell students that the rectangle is equal to one whole. Divide the rectangle in half and shade one part of the rectangle. Ask students to identify the fraction name for the shaded part of the rectangle. Write the fraction $\frac{1}{2}$ under the shaded part of the rectangle as shown in Figure 2.

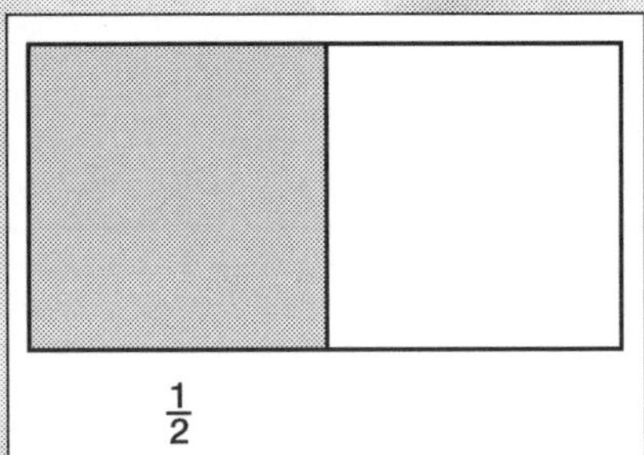

Figure 2: *$\frac{1}{2}$ of a rectangle*

Draw a second rectangle and divide it into two obviously unequal pieces as shown in Figure 3. Ask:

- *Does each of these parts also equal $\frac{1}{2}$?* (These pieces do not equal $\frac{1}{2}$ because they are not equal shares.)

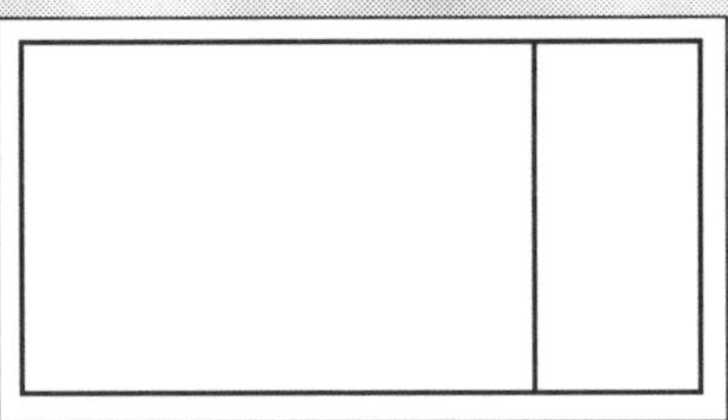

Figure 3: *This rectangle is not divided in half.*

If you feel students need other examples of fractions, draw additional rectangles, dividing them to represent various fractions. For example:

- Divide a rectangle into four equal parts. Shade in one part or $\frac{1}{4}$ of the rectangle and ask students to identify how much of the rectangle is shaded. Ask students to identify the fraction of the rectangle that is not shaded ($\frac{3}{4}$).
- Divide a rectangle into three equal parts. Shade in two parts or $\frac{2}{3}$ of the rectangle and ask students to identify how much of the rectangle is shaded. How much of the rectangle is not shaded?

Another way to review fractions is to ask five students, some boys and some girls, to stand in the front of the room. Ask students to identify the fraction of the students who are boys and the fraction who are girls. This activity can be repeated using a different number of students or different attributes each time. For example:

- *What fraction of the students standing have brown hair?*
- *What fraction of the students standing are wearing red today?*

As students call out fractions, write them on the board. Identify the bottom number of each fraction as the **denominator.** Explain that the denominator tells you the number of equal pieces (or parts) into which the whole is divided. Identify the top number of each fraction as the **numerator.** Explain that the numerator tells you how many pieces (or parts) you are interested in.

Developing the Activity

Part 1. Halves, Fourths, and Eighths

Once students have reviewed what a fraction is, begin the paper-folding activity. Students will complete Lesson 1 over three days. They will use their strips during Lesson 2 to add and subtract fractions with like denominators, during Lesson 3 to compare fractions, during Lesson 4 as a chart to play *Frabble,* and during Lesson 5 as a chart to explore equivalent fractions.

Have students work with partners or in small groups so that they can discuss strategies. They can also check each other's folds for accuracy.

Pass out an envelope for storing strips to each student. Have students carefully cut out all of the strips on the *Making Fraction Strips* Activity Pages in the *Discovery Assignment Book.* Students will use four of the strips during Part 1. They will identify one strip as a whole and fold the other three into halves, fourths, and eighths. Completed strips should be color-coded. Extra strips can be stored in the envelopes provided.

> **TIMS Tip**
>
> Decide on a common color code for your classroom. For example, have all the students color their strips showing halves red, their strips showing fourths brown, etc. Using the colors used on the Fraction Chart on the *Comparing Fractions* Activity Page (Lesson 3) in the *Student Guide* may reduce confusion and make it easier for students to remember the color code. (Note that the colors for the whole, halves, fourths, and sixths correspond to the pattern blocks that represent those fractions when the yellow hexagon is one whole.) With all the students using strips of the same color, it will be easier to monitor the activities in this lesson. Instruct students to color strips lightly, since they will write the names of the fractions on the strips.

The first step in the activity is to establish that an unfolded strip of paper represents one whole. Tell each student to label an unfolded strip as one whole and set this aside.

Explain to students that they will fold each strip to show different fractions. Have students fold a strip into two pieces that are exactly the same size. Make sure that students crease their strips carefully, mak-

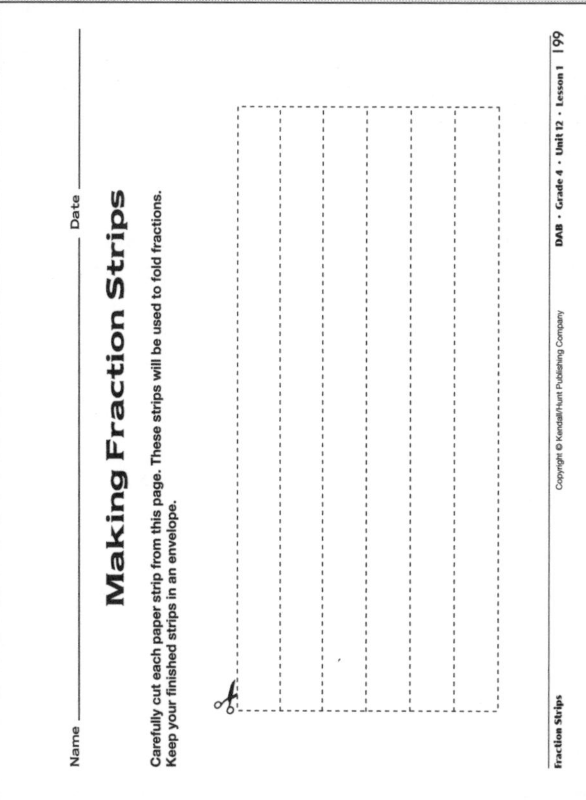

Discovery Assignment Book - Page 199

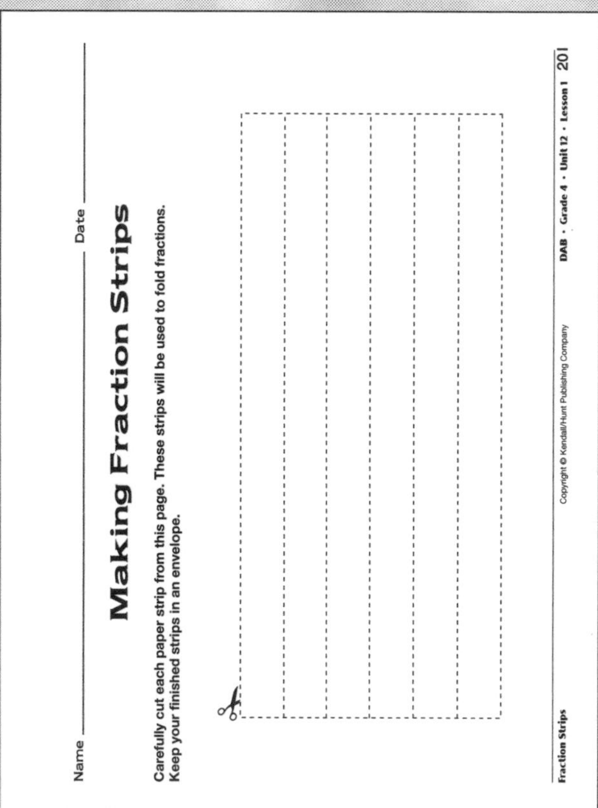

Discovery Assignment Book - Page 201

Each student has been provided with two extra strips. These can be used if a student loses a strip or makes an error folding. Fraction strips can also be made from construction paper or card stock. Strips should each be 20 cm in length. Each student will need 10 strips of different colors.

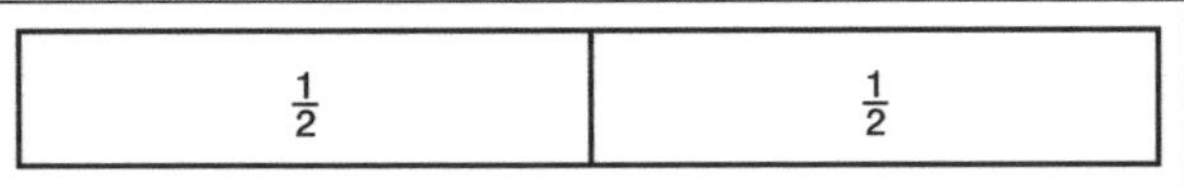

Figure 4: *A paper strip folded into halves*

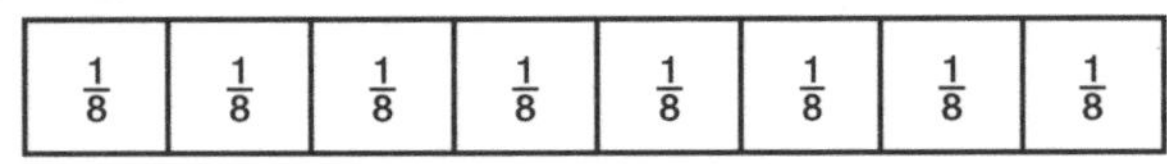

Figure 5: *A fraction strip showing eighths*

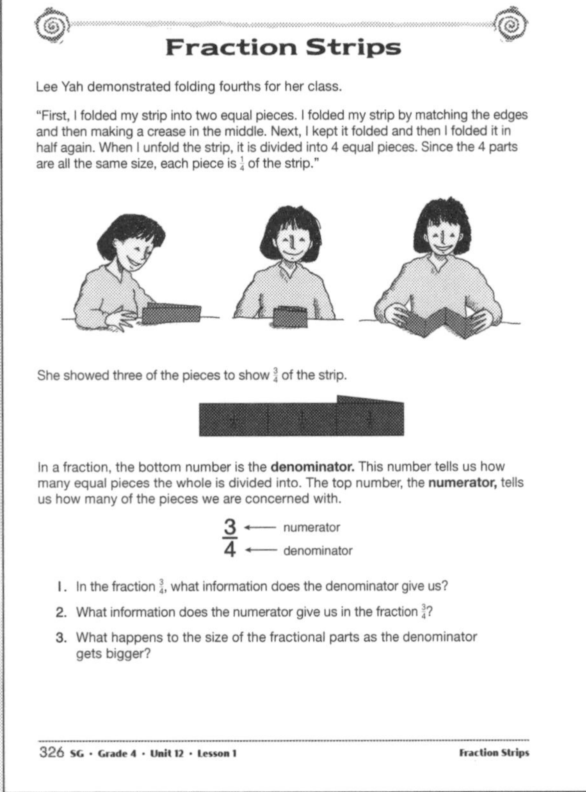

Fraction Strips

Lee Yah demonstrated folding fourths for her class.

"First, I folded my strip into two equal pieces. I folded my strip by matching the edges and then making a crease in the middle. Next, I kept it folded and then I folded it in half again. When I unfold the strip, it is divided into 4 equal pieces. Since the 4 parts are all the same size, each piece is $\frac{1}{4}$ of the strip."

She showed three of the pieces to show $\frac{3}{4}$ of the strip.

In a fraction, the bottom number is the **denominator.** This number tells us how many equal pieces the whole is divided into. The top number, the **numerator,** tells us how many of the pieces we are concerned with.

$\frac{3}{4}$ ← numerator, ← denominator

1. In the fraction $\frac{3}{4}$, what information does the denominator give us?
2. What information does the numerator give us in the fraction $\frac{3}{4}$?
3. What happens to the size of the fractional parts as the denominator gets bigger?

326 SG • Grade 4 • Unit 12 • Lesson 1 Fraction Strips

***Student Guide* - Page 326**

ing clean sharp folds. Once the folding is completed, ask students to unfold their strips and draw a line with a ruler showing their folds. Ask:

- *What is the fraction name for each part of this strip?* ($\frac{1}{2}$)
- *What is the* ***denominator*** *and what does it tell us?* (2, how many parts the whole was divided into)
- *What is the* ***numerator*** *and what does it tell us?* (1, how many of the parts we are concerned with)

Have students color their strips according to the color code decided upon and label each part $\frac{1}{2}$. See Figure 4.

Next, ask students how they can fold a different strip into four equal pieces. Allow students a minute or two to discuss this with the members of their groups. Students can first fold their strips in half and then in half again. When they unfold their strips, they will have four equal pieces. After students have completed their folds, ask them to unfold their strips and use their rulers to draw a line showing each fold. Ask students what the denominator will be for each fraction on this strip. Students then color their strips and label each piece with $\frac{1}{4}$.

Next, students fold a strip into eight equal pieces. Have them discuss a method for doing this within their groups. The most efficient method is first to fold the strip in half, then fold the folded strip in half again, and finally fold this in half. When the strip is unfolded, it will be in eight equal sections. Review the same questions as used above for halves. Students should color and label as in Figure 5.

Questions 1–3 on the *Fraction Strips* Activity Pages in the *Student Guide* review what a fraction is, the definition of the denominator, and the definition of the numerator. These pages can be used at any time during this lesson to review these concepts.

Show Me. In this activity, students use their fraction strips to represent different fractions. Students will need all their completed strips and the strip representing one whole. To start this activity, name a fraction that can be represented using the fraction strips; for example, $\frac{3}{8}$. To show $\frac{3}{8}$, students should use the strip that is divided into eight equal pieces. They fold $\frac{5}{8}$ of the strip back and leave $\frac{3}{8}$ of the strip showing as in Figure 6.

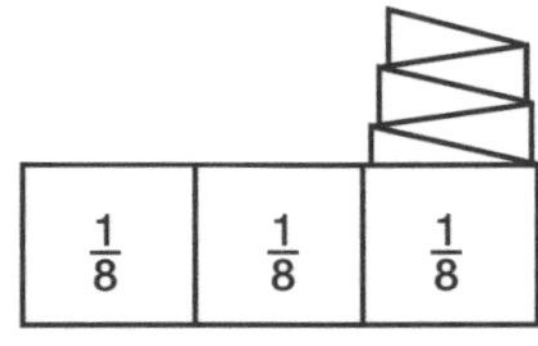

Figure 6: *Folding a strip to show $\frac{3}{8}$*

Continue this activity by asking students to show you fractions that are less than one, for example, $\frac{1}{4}$, $\frac{5}{8}$, $\frac{1}{2}$, $\frac{2}{4}$, $\frac{3}{4}$.

Once students are comfortable using their strips to show fractions less than one, move on to fractions equivalent to one, such as $\frac{4}{4}$ and $\frac{2}{2}$. Finally, ask students to show mixed numbers—for example, $1\frac{1}{2}$. *Note:* To show $1\frac{1}{2}$, students will need to use two of their strips, the strip showing one whole and the strip showing halves.

For a variation of this activity, hold up one of the marked fraction strips that you prepared before class. Then, fold it to represent a fraction and ask students to identify the name of that fraction. If students are unable to name the fraction, unfold the strip and ask students to identify the number of parts into which the whole strip is divided (the denominator), then refold the strip to show your fraction and ask how many parts you are showing them (the numerator). Remind students of the definitions of denominator and numerator. Again ask students to name the fraction that you are holding.

Homework ***Questions 1–7*** in the *Student Guide* can be assigned at this point in the lesson.

Part 2. Thirds, Sixths, Ninths, and Twelfths
During this part of the lesson, students will use four more of their strips, folding them into thirds, sixths, ninths, and twelfths. Ask students to take one of their strips and to think about how they can fold it into three equal parts. Students may suggest first folding the strip into a loose "S" and then carefully matching edges before creasing the folds. Students may also suggest folding the paper like a letter. Both techniques are shown in Figure 7.

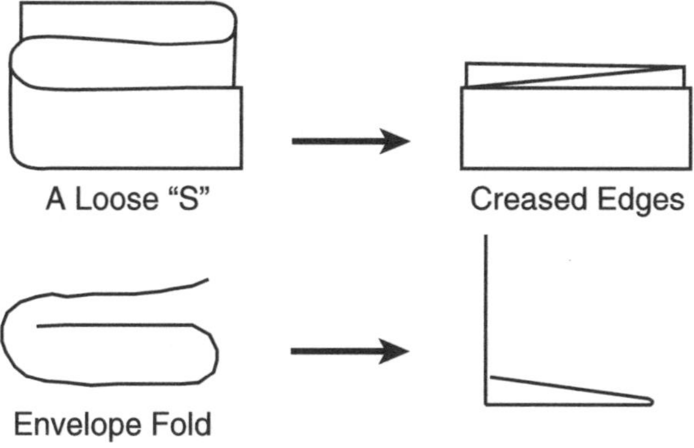

Figure 7: *Folding a strip to show thirds*

Folding strips into thirds is more difficult than the previous folding, so monitor each student's progress carefully. This process may require some trial and

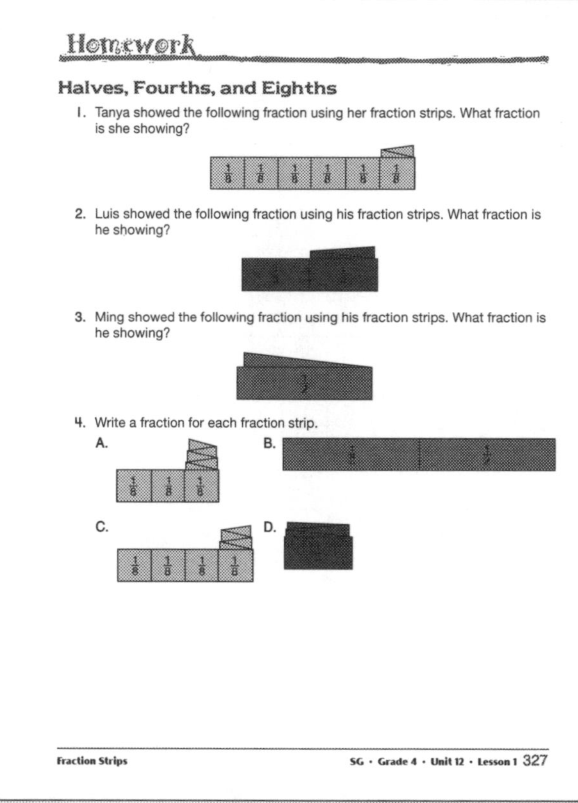

Homework

Halves, Fourths, and Eighths

1. Tanya showed the following fraction using her fraction strips. What fraction is she showing?
2. Luis showed the following fraction using his fraction strips. What fraction is he showing?
3. Ming showed the following fraction using his fraction strips. What fraction is he showing?
4. Write a fraction for each fraction strip.
   A.
   B.
   C.
   D.

Fraction Strips SG · Grade 4 · Unit 12 · Lesson 1 327

***Student Guide* - Page 327**

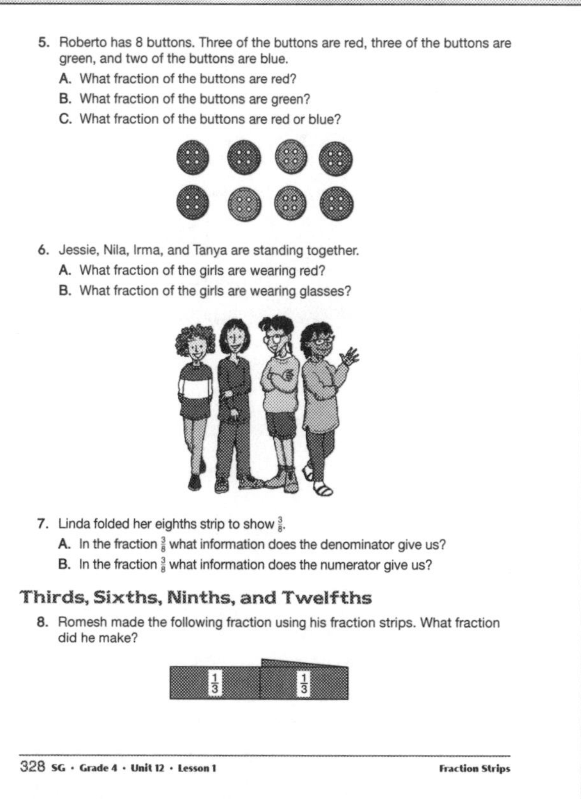

5. Roberto has 8 buttons. Three of the buttons are red, three of the buttons are green, and two of the buttons are blue.
   A. What fraction of the buttons are red?
   B. What fraction of the buttons are green?
   C. What fraction of the buttons are red or blue?
6. Jessie, Nila, Irma, and Tanya are standing together.
   A. What fraction of the girls are wearing red?
   B. What fraction of the girls are wearing glasses?
7. Linda folded her eighths strip to show $\frac{3}{8}$.
   A. In the fraction $\frac{3}{8}$ what information does the denominator give us?
   B. In the fraction $\frac{3}{8}$ what information does the numerator give us?

Thirds, Sixths, Ninths, and Twelfths

8. Romesh made the following fraction using his fraction strips. What fraction did he make?

328 SG · Grade 4 · Unit 12 · Lesson 1 Fraction Strips

***Student Guide* - Page 328**

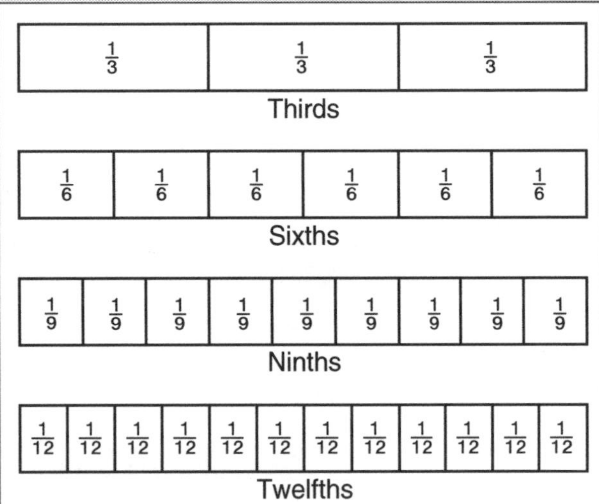

Figure 8: *Thirds, sixths, ninths, and twelfths*

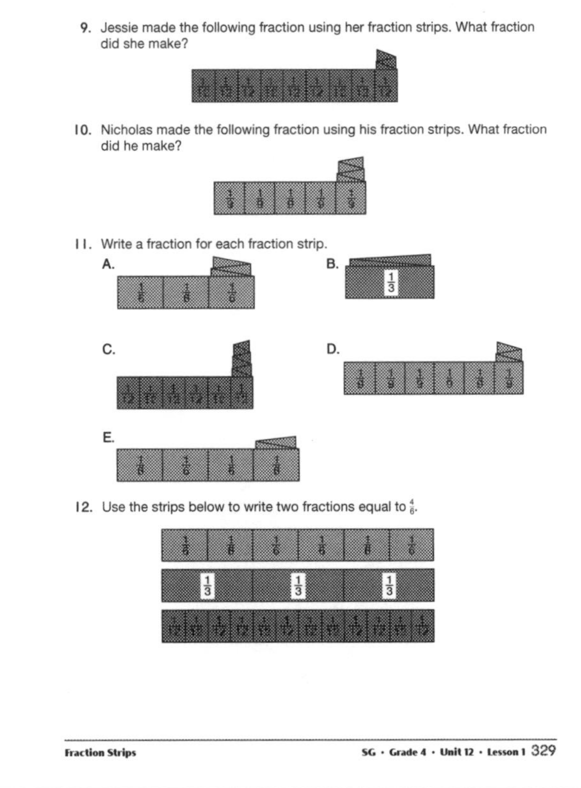

9. Jessie made the following fraction using her fraction strips. What fraction did she make?

10. Nicholas made the following fraction using his fraction strips. What fraction did he make?

11. Write a fraction for each fraction strip.
A. B.
C. D.
E.

12. Use the strips below to write two fractions equal to $\frac{4}{6}$.

Fraction Strips SG • Grade 4 • Unit 12 • Lesson 1 329

***Student Guide* - Page 329**

Content Note

Equivalent Fractions. In mathematics, two fractions that have the same value are considered equivalent fractions. On the fraction strips, equivalent fractions are two that show the same length. This term is discussed more fully in Lesson 5 of this unit, after the students have become more familiar with the basic concepts of fractions. At the fourth grade level, we do not distinguish between the words equal and equivalent. Therefore, it is acceptable for students to use either equal or equivalent when comparing two fractions that have the same value.

error. Students should mark each fold with a line, color their strips, and label each piece $\frac{1}{3}$. Continue this lesson by asking students to discuss methods for folding one strip into six equal pieces or sixths, one strip into nine equal pieces or ninths, and one strip into twelve equal pieces or twelfths.

Students can fold a strip into sixths by first folding it into thirds and then folding the folded strip in half. Students can also start by folding their strips in half and then folding the halves into thirds.

To fold a strip into ninths, students can first fold a strip into thirds and then fold it into thirds again.

A strip can be folded into twelfths by first folding it into thirds, then folding the folded strip in half, and finally folding it in half again, or the strip can first be folded in half, then thirds, and finally in half again. As students fold each strip, they should mark their folds with a line, color, and label each strip with the correct fraction name as shown in Figure 8.

Students have now completed strips to show one whole, halves, thirds, fourths, sixths, eighths, ninths, and twelfths. Ask students to lay all eight strips out on their desks. You can now extend Show Me, described in Part 1 of this lesson, to include all eight strips.

Equivalent Fractions. This part of the activity will initially be teacher-led. However, once students are comfortable with this procedure, they can work with a partner to find equivalent fractions. Ask:

- *Fold your halves strips to show $\frac{1}{2}$. Find and fold all the other strips that can be folded to show the same quantity.*

Remind students that strips can only be folded on existing fraction lines. Figure 9 illustrates those fraction strips that can be folded to show fractions equal to $\frac{1}{2}$.

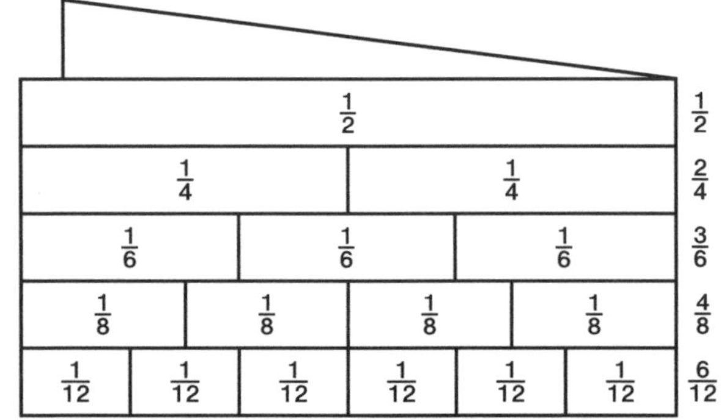

Figure 9: *Folding fractions equivalent to $\frac{1}{2}$*

List all the equivalencies on the chalkboard. The list should include $\frac{1}{2}$, $\frac{2}{4}$, $\frac{3}{6}$, $\frac{4}{8}$, and $\frac{6}{12}$. Explain that these are called **equivalent fractions** because they each show the same part of the whole. Ask:

- *Which strips cannot be folded on existing fraction lines to show an equivalent fraction for $\frac{1}{2}$?* (Students will see that the strip divided into thirds and the strip divided into ninths cannot be used to show a fraction equivalent to $\frac{1}{2}$.)
- *Look at the denominators of the strips that can be used to show a fraction equivalent to $\frac{1}{2}$ and then at the strips that could not be used to show an equivalent fraction. What can you say about the denominators that can be used to show fractions equivalent to $\frac{1}{2}$?*

Guide students to see that when the denominator is a multiple of two, a fraction equivalent to $\frac{1}{2}$ can be found, but when the denominator is not a multiple of two there is not an equivalent fraction with that denominator. Continue this activity in a similar fashion with $\frac{1}{3}$ and $\frac{1}{4}$.

- *What are all the fractions that are equivalent to $\frac{1}{3}$?* ($\frac{2}{6}$, $\frac{3}{9}$, $\frac{4}{12}$)
- *What do you notice about the denominators?* (They are all multiples of 3.)

Suggest other fractions for the students to find equivalent fractions, e.g., $\frac{1}{4}$, $\frac{3}{4}$, $\frac{2}{3}$, $\frac{5}{6}$, etc.

Homework ***Questions 8–13*** in the Homework section of the *Student Guide* can be assigned at this time.

Part 3. Fifths and Tenths

Students will use two of the strips left from Parts 1 and 2 of this lesson, folding one strip into five equal pieces or fifths and one strip into ten equal pieces or tenths. Ask students for a strategy to fold a strip into five equal pieces. Students will probably realize that this is a very difficult task without something to guide them. Students may suggest using their rulers to find out how long each strip is. They can then divide to find out how long each piece should be. The strips are each 20 cm

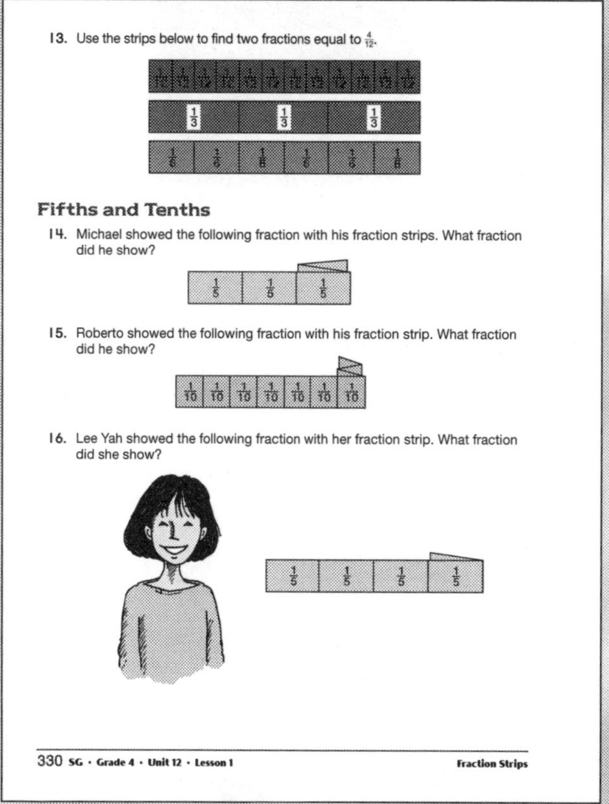

13. Use the strips below to find two fractions equal to $\frac{4}{12}$.

Fifths and Tenths

14. Michael showed the following fraction with his fraction strips. What fraction did he show?

15. Roberto showed the following fraction with his fraction strip. What fraction did he show?

16. Lee Yah showed the following fraction with her fraction strip. What fraction did she show?

330 SG · Grade 4 · Unit 12 · Lesson 1 Fraction Strips

***Student Guide* - Page 330**

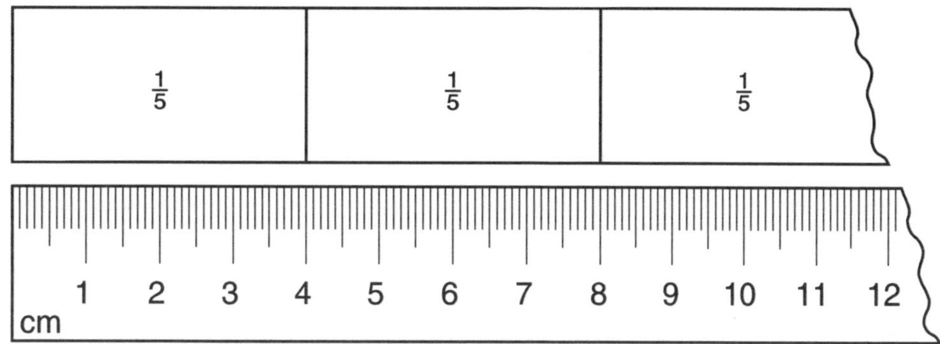

Figure 10: *Measuring 5 equal pieces*

long. This means that when dividing into fifths, each piece should be four cm long and when dividing into tenths, each piece should be two cm long. Students can use their rulers to mark each fold before making the creases. This method is shown in Figure 10. Make sure students draw lines to show their folds, color their strips, and label each $\frac{1}{5}$.

To fold a strip into ten equal pieces, students can first fold their strips into fifths and then fold these folded strips in half. Students can also use their rulers to find where each fold should be. Students should mark folds, color, and label as before.

Students now have a complete set of fraction strips. This set should include one whole strip and strips folded into 2, 3, 4, 5, 6, 8, 9, 10, and 12 equal pieces. Extend the Show Me activity described in Part 1 of this lesson and Equivalent Fractions described in Part 2 using the complete set of fraction strips. Store the fraction strips in envelopes for use during Lessons 2–3.

Assign ***Questions 14–21*** in the Homework section of the *Student Guide* at this time.

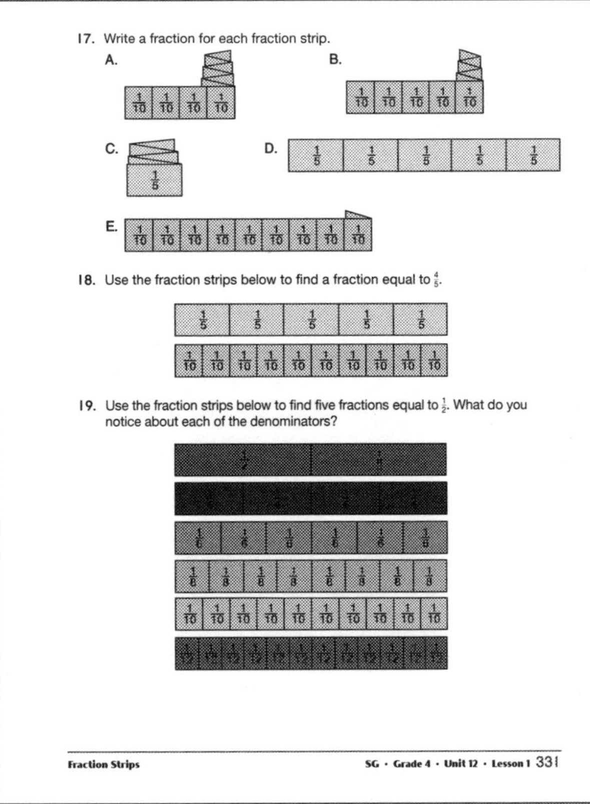

17. Write a fraction for each fraction strip.

A. B. C. D. E.

18. Use the fraction strips below to find a fraction equal to $\frac{4}{5}$.

19. Use the fraction strips below to find five fractions equal to $\frac{1}{2}$. What do you notice about each of the denominators?

Fraction Strips SG • Grade 4 • Unit 12 • Lesson 1 331

***Student Guide* - Page 331**

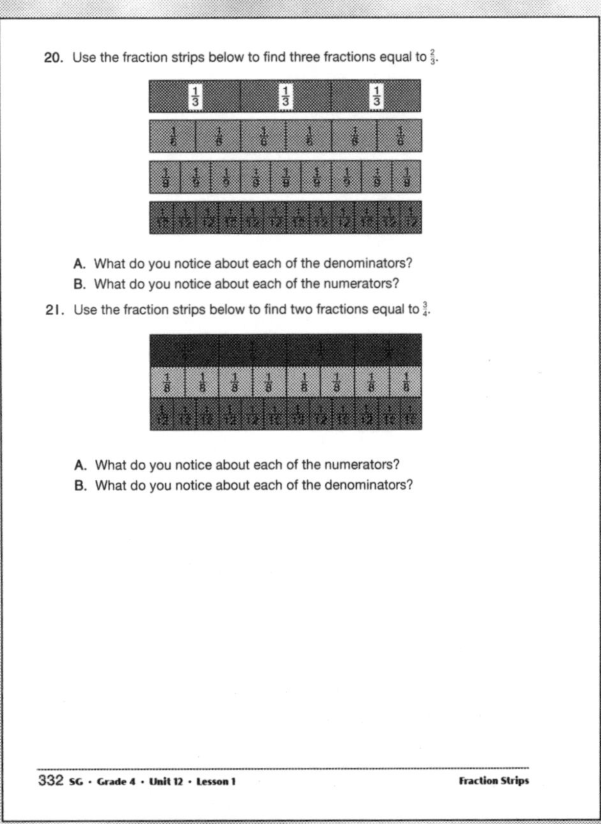

20. Use the fraction strips below to find three fractions equal to $\frac{2}{3}$.

A. What do you notice about each of the denominators?

B. What do you notice about each of the numerators?

21. Use the fraction strips below to find two fractions equal to $\frac{3}{4}$.

A. What do you notice about each of the numerators?

B. What do you notice about each of the denominators?

332 SG • Grade 4 • Unit 12 • Lesson 1 Fraction Strips

***Student Guide* - Page 332**

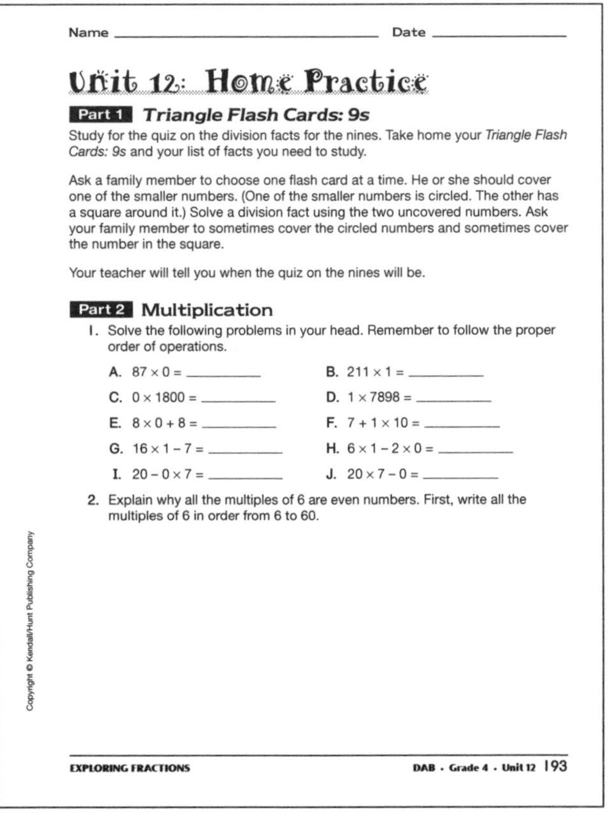

Name ______________________ Date ____________

Unit 12: Home Practice

Part 1 ***Triangle Flash Cards: 9s***

Study for the quiz on the division facts for the nines. Take home your *Triangle Flash Cards: 9s* and your list of facts you need to study.

Ask a family member to choose one flash card at a time. He or she should cover one of the smaller numbers. (One of the smaller numbers is circled. The other has a square around it.) Solve a division fact using the two uncovered numbers. Ask your family member to sometimes cover the circled numbers and sometimes cover the number in the square.

Your teacher will tell you when the quiz on the nines will be.

Part 2 **Multiplication**

1. Solve the following problems in your head. Remember to follow the proper order of operations.

A. $87 \times 0 =$ ________ B. $211 \times 1 =$ ________

C. $0 \times 1800 =$ ________ D. $1 \times 7898 =$ ________

E. $8 \times 0 + 8 =$ ________ F. $7 + 1 \times 10 =$ ________

G. $16 \times 1 - 7 =$ ________ H. $6 \times 1 - 2 \times 0 =$ ________

I. $20 - 0 \times 7 =$ ________ J. $20 \times 7 - 0 =$ ________

2. Explain why all the multiples of 6 are even numbers. First, write all the multiples of 6 in order from 6 to 60.

EXPLORING FRACTIONS DAB • Grade 4 • Unit 12 193

***Discovery Assignment Book* - Page 193**

Suggestions for Teaching the Lesson

Math Facts

- Use DPP items B and C to begin the review and practice of the division facts for the nines.
- Part 1 of the Home Practice reminds students to take home their flash cards to practice the facts.

Homework and Practice

- Assign the homework questions in the *Student Guide* as appropriate. ***Questions 1–7*** can be assigned after Part 1, ***Questions 8–13*** after Part 2, ***Questions 14–21*** after Part 3.
- DPP items A and F provide practice with elapsed time. Use Task D for practice with multidigit multiplication. DPP Bit E requires students to extend a pattern using decimals.
- Assign Part 2 of the Home Practice.

Answers for Part 2 of the Home Practice can be found in the Answer Key at the end of this lesson and at the end of this unit.

Assessment

Use the *Observational Assessment Record* to document students' abilities to represent fractions using paper folding.

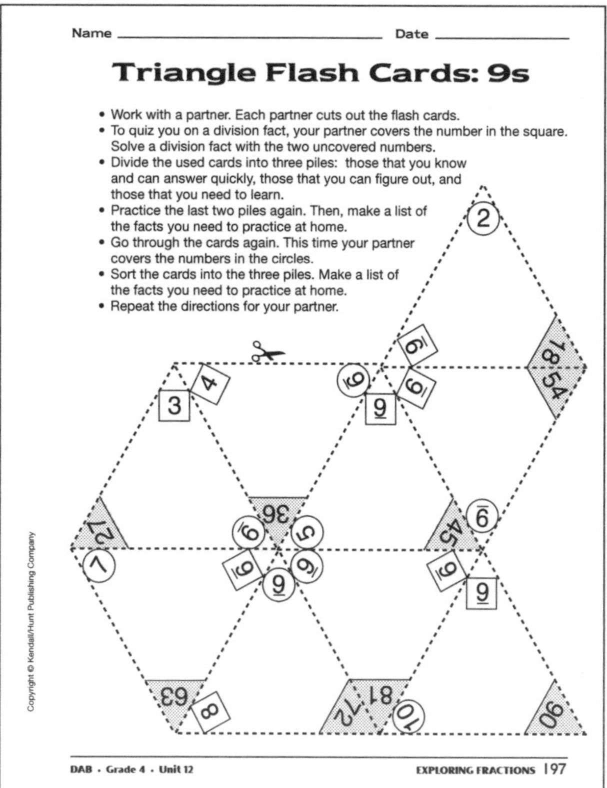

Name ______________________ Date ____________

Triangle Flash Cards: 9s

- Work with a partner. Each partner cuts out the flash cards.
- To quiz you on a division fact, your partner covers the number in the square. Solve a division fact with the two uncovered numbers.
- Divide the used cards into three piles: those that you know and can answer quickly, those that you can figure out, and those that you need to learn.
- Practice the last two piles again. Then, make a list of the facts you need to practice at home.
- Go through the cards again. This time your partner covers the numbers in the circles.
- Sort the cards into the three piles. Make a list of the facts you need to practice at home.
- Repeat the directions for your partner.

Copyright © Kendall/Hunt Publishing Company

DAB • Grade 4 • Unit 12 EXPLORING FRACTIONS 197

Discovery Assignment Book - **Page 197**

Daily Practice and Problems: Tasks for Lesson 1

B. Task: Division Facts: 9s (URG p. 13)

With a partner, use your *Triangle Flash Cards: 9s* to quiz each other on the division facts for the nines. Ask your partner first to cover the numbers in the squares. Use the two uncovered numbers to solve a division fact. Separate the flash cards into three piles: those facts you know and can answer quickly, those that you can figure out with a strategy, and those that you need to learn.

Then, go through the cards again and have your partner cover the numbers in the circles. Use the uncovered numbers to solve a division fact. Separate the cards into three piles again.

Both times through, practice the facts that are in the last two piles and make a list of these facts so that you can practice them at home.

Circle all the facts you know and can answer quickly on your *Division Facts I Know* chart.

Repeat this process for your partner.

D. Task: Multiplication (URG p. 14)

Use paper and pencil or mental math to solve the following problems. Estimate to make sure your answers are reasonable.

1. A. $53 \times 4 =$ B. $459 \times 4 =$
   C. $5532 \times 4 =$ D. $26 \times 45 =$
   E. $22 \times 7 =$ F. $724 \times 3 =$
   G. $3096 \times 5 =$ H. $38 \times 52 =$
2. Explain your strategy for Question 1A.
3. Explain your estimation strategy for Question 1D.

F. Task: Earning an Allowance (URG p. 15)

Irma's aunt pays her 5 cents each minute she reads a book instead of watching television. She began reading at 4:48 and finished at 5:19. How much money did she make? Tell the strategies you used to get your answer.

AT A GLANCE

Math Facts and Daily Practice and Problems

DPP items B and C and Home Practice Part 1 review and practice the division facts for the nines. DPP Items A and F provide practice with time. DPP Task D practices multiplication and DPP Bit E asks students to extend a decimal pattern.

Before the Activity

1. Use the *Fraction Strips for the Teacher* Blackline Masters to make one set of fraction strips for demonstration.
2. Review fractions using fractions on the chalkboard. Define numerator and denominator.
3. Model fractions of a set with a group of students.

Part 1. Halves, Fourths, and Eighths

1. Students cut out 20-cm paper strips on the *Making Fraction Strips* Activity Pages in the *Discovery Assignment Book.*
2. Students label one strip as a whole and set this aside.
3. Each student folds one strip into two equal pieces, marks the fold, labels each piece $\frac{1}{2}$, and colors the strip.
4. Students follow the same procedure to make strips for fourths and eighths.
5. Introduce the Show Me activity, in which the teacher names a fraction and the students show the same fraction using the strips.
6. Use the first *Fraction Strips* Activity Page in the *Student Guide* to review the definition of numerator and denominator.

Part 2. Thirds, Sixths, Ninths, and Twelfths

1. Students follow the above procedure to make strips for thirds, sixths, ninths, and twelfths. Extend Show Me to include all eight of their strips.
2. Introduce Equivalent Fractions, in which the teacher names a fraction and students find all the equivalent fractions that can be made using their strips.

Part 3. Fifths and Tenths

1. Students use their rulers to divide one strip into fifths and one strip into tenths.
2. Students color each strip and label each piece with the correct fraction name.
3. Extend Show Me and Equivalent Fractions to include all ten strips.
4. Save all strips in envelopes for use during Lessons 2–5.

Homework

1. Assign homework ***Questions 1–7*** in the *Student Guide* any time after Part 1, homework ***Questions 8–13*** after Part 2, and homework ***Questions 14–21*** after Part 3.
2. Students take their flash cards home to study the division facts for the nines.
3. Assign Home Practice Part 2 in the *Discovery Assignment Book.*

AT A GLANCE

Assessment

Use the *Observational Assessment Record* to record students' abilities to represent fractions with paper folding.

Notes:

Fraction Strips for the Teacher

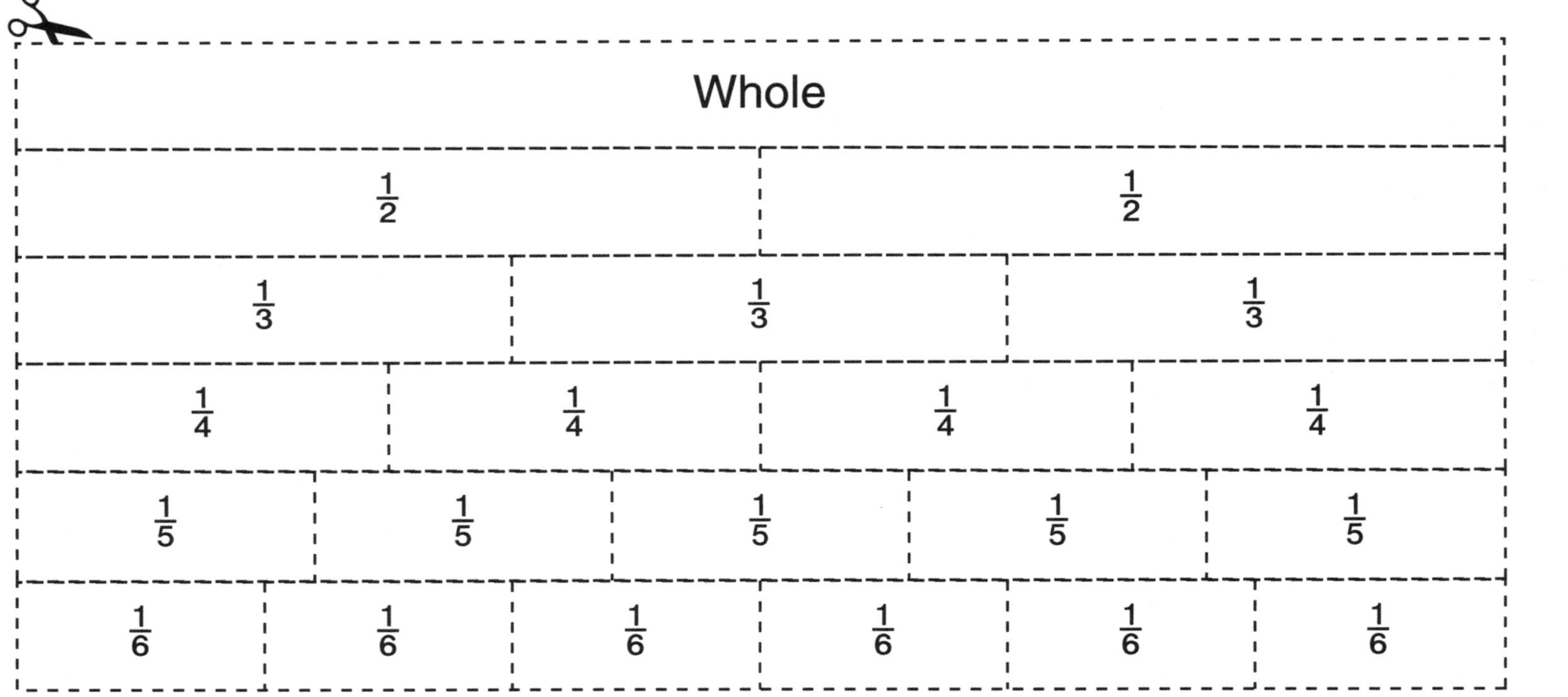

Fraction Strips for the Teacher

$\frac{1}{8}$ $\frac{1}{8}$ $\frac{1}{8}$ $\frac{1}{8}$ $\frac{1}{8}$ $\frac{1}{8}$ $\frac{1}{8}$ $\frac{1}{8}$

$\frac{1}{9}$ $\frac{1}{9}$ $\frac{1}{9}$ $\frac{1}{9}$ $\frac{1}{9}$ $\frac{1}{9}$ $\frac{1}{9}$ $\frac{1}{9}$ $\frac{1}{9}$

$\frac{1}{10}$ $\frac{1}{10}$ $\frac{1}{10}$ $\frac{1}{10}$ $\frac{1}{10}$ $\frac{1}{10}$ $\frac{1}{10}$ $\frac{1}{10}$ $\frac{1}{10}$ $\frac{1}{10}$

$\frac{1}{12}$ $\frac{1}{12}$ $\frac{1}{12}$ $\frac{1}{12}$ $\frac{1}{12}$ $\frac{1}{12}$ $\frac{1}{12}$ $\frac{1}{12}$ $\frac{1}{12}$ $\frac{1}{12}$ $\frac{1}{12}$ $\frac{1}{12}$

Student Guide

Questions 1–3 (SG p. 326)

1. The denominator tells the number of equal parts into which the whole is divided.
2. The numerator tells how many parts you are interested in.
3. The fraction gets smaller.

Homework (SG pp. 327–332)

Questions 1–21

1. $\frac{6}{8}$
2. $\frac{2}{4}$
3. $\frac{1}{2}$
4. **A.** $\frac{3}{8}$
   B. $\frac{2}{2}$ or 1
   C. $\frac{4}{8}$
   D. $\frac{1}{4}$
5. **A.** $\frac{3}{8}$
   B. $\frac{3}{8}$
   C. $\frac{5}{8}$
6. **A.** $\frac{3}{4}$
   B. $\frac{2}{4}$ or $\frac{1}{2}$
7. **A.** The denominator tells us that the fraction strip is divided into 8 equal pieces.
   B. The numerator tells us that she is showing 3 of the 8 pieces.
8. $\frac{2}{3}$
9. $\frac{9}{12}$
10. $\frac{5}{9}$
11. **A.** $\frac{3}{6}$
    B. $\frac{1}{3}$
    C. $\frac{6}{12}$
    D. $\frac{6}{9}$
    E. $\frac{4}{6}$
12. $\frac{2}{3}, \frac{8}{12}$
13. $\frac{1}{3}, \frac{2}{6}$
14. $\frac{3}{5}$
15. $\frac{7}{10}$
16. $\frac{4}{5}$
17. **A.** $\frac{4}{10}$
    B. $\frac{5}{10}$ or $\frac{1}{2}$
    C. $\frac{1}{5}$
    D. $\frac{5}{5}$ or 1
    E. $\frac{9}{10}$
18. $\frac{8}{10}$
19. $\frac{2}{4}, \frac{3}{6}, \frac{4}{8}, \frac{5}{10}, \frac{6}{12}$
    Each of the denominators is even and, therefore, a multiple of 2.
20. $\frac{4}{6}, \frac{6}{9}, \frac{8}{12}$
    A. Each of the denominators is a multiple of 3.
    B. Each of the numerators is even and, therefore, a multiple of 2.
21. $\frac{6}{8}, \frac{9}{12}$
    A. Both of the numerators are multiples of 3.
    B. Both of the denominators are multiples of 4.

Discovery Assignment Book

**** Home Practice (DAB p. 193)**

Part 2. Multiplication

Question 1–2

1. **A.** 0 **B.** 211
   C. 0 **D.** 7898
   E. 8 **F.** 17
   G. 9 **H.** 6
   I. 20 **J.** 140
2. 6, 12, 18, 24, 30, 36, 42, 48, 54, 60
   An even number has 2 as a factor. Since 2 is a factor of 6, 2 is a factor of all the multiples of 6. So, all the multiples of 6 are even numbers.

*Answers and/or discussion are included in the Lesson Guide.
**Answers for all the Home Practice in the *Discovery Assignment Book* are at the end of the unit.

LESSON GUIDE 

Adding and Subtracting with Fraction Strips

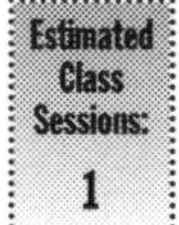

Estimated Class Sessions: 1

Students use their fraction strips from Lesson 1 to add and subtract fractions with like denominators.

Key Content

- Adding and subtracting fractions with like denominators.

Daily Practice and Problems: Bit for Lesson 2

G. More Division Facts (URG p. 15) 

Find the number n that makes the sentence true.

A. $72 \div 8 = n$ B. $n \div 9 = 6$

C. $n \div 9 = 5$ D. $36 \div 4 = n$

E. $27 \div n = 9$ F. $n \div 9 = 9$

G. $n \div 9 = 2$ H. $63 \div n = 9$

The DPP Task is on page 41. Suggestions for using the DPPs are on page 41.

Materials List

Print Materials for Students

		Math Facts and Daily Practice and Problems	Activity	Homework
Student Book	Student Guide		*Adding and Subtracting with Fraction Strips* Pages 333–334	*Adding and Subtracting with Fraction Strips* Homework Section Page 335
Teacher Resources	Facts Resource Guide (CD)	DPP Items 12G & 12H		
Teacher Resources	Unit Resource Guide	DPP Items G–H Page 15 (CD)		

(CD) *available on Teacher Resource CD*

All Transparency Masters, Blackline Masters, and Assessment Blackline Masters in the Unit Resource Guide are on the Teacher Resource CD.

Supplies for Each Student

set of fraction strips from Lesson 1

Materials for the Teacher

Fraction Strips for the Teacher Blackline Masters (Unit Resource Guide) Pages 36–37, 1 set of cut strips, folded, colored, and labeled

Observational Assessment Record (Unit Resource Guide, Pages 9–10 and Teacher Resource CD)

Adding and Subtracting with Fraction Strips

Mrs. Dewey asked her class to use their fraction strips to add $\frac{1}{4}$ and $\frac{2}{4}$. Keenya explained her solution to the class:

"First, I folded my strip that shows fourths so that 1 piece or $\frac{1}{4}$ of the strip was showing. Then, I added $\frac{2}{4}$ of the strip by unfolding 2 more pieces. I ended up with $\frac{3}{4}$ of my strip showing. So, $\frac{1}{4} + \frac{2}{4} = \frac{3}{4}$."

Next, Mrs. Dewey asked the class to use their fraction strips to subtract $\frac{3}{8}$ from $\frac{7}{8}$.

Jacob explained his solution to the class:

"I started with my strip that is divided into eighths. I folded it so that $\frac{7}{8}$ of the strip was showing. Then, I folded $\frac{3}{8}$ of the strip or 3 more pieces of the strip back since I was subtracting. This left me with $\frac{4}{8}$ of the strip showing, so $\frac{7}{8} - \frac{3}{8} = \frac{4}{8}$."

Adding and Subtracting with Fraction Strips SG • Grade 4 • Unit 12 • Lesson 2 333

Student Guide - Page 333

Work with a partner to solve the following problems. You will need to use two sets of fraction strips. Write a number sentence for each problem.

1. Maya has $\frac{5}{8}$ of a yard of fabric. She needs $\frac{3}{8}$ of a yard of fabric for a craft project. How much fabric will she have left over after she completes her project?
2. Frank is baking a cake. The recipe calls for $\frac{1}{4}$ cup of oil and $\frac{3}{4}$ cup of water. How much liquid will Frank add to the cake mix?
3. Jessie used $\frac{5}{12}$ of a board for a sign. What fraction of the board is left for another project?
4. There was $\frac{5}{6}$ of a pie on the counter when Luis got home from school.
   A. Luis ate $\frac{2}{6}$ of the pie. How much of the pie is left?
   B. Luis's sister ate another $\frac{1}{6}$ of the pie. Now how much of the pie is left?
   C. Use your fraction strips to find another fraction that is equal to your answer to Question 4B.
5. Ming rode his bike $\frac{8}{10}$ mile to Frank's house. He then rode $\frac{8}{10}$ mile back home again. How far did Ming ride altogether?

6. Irma must finish her homework and practice piano before she can go outside to play. It takes her $\frac{3}{4}$ hour to do her homework and she practices piano for $\frac{2}{4}$ hour. How long does she have to wait before going outside to play?
7. Use your fraction strips to complete the following number sentences.
   A. $\frac{3}{8} + \frac{2}{8} =$ B. $\frac{7}{10} + \frac{5}{10} =$ C. $\frac{3}{6} + \frac{3}{6} =$
   D. $\frac{11}{12} - \frac{4}{12} =$ E. $\frac{3}{5} - \frac{1}{5} =$ F. $\frac{7}{8} - \frac{3}{8} =$

334 SG • Grade 4 • Unit 12 • Lesson 2 Adding and Subtracting with Fraction Strips

Student Guide - Page 334

Developing the Activity

Introduce this lesson by reading the short vignette on the *Adding and Subtracting with Fraction Strips* Activity Pages in the *Student Guide.* Students can then use their fraction strips to complete ***Questions 1–7***. Students should work with a partner as two sets of fraction strips are needed for some of the questions. Students complete the questions and then share their solutions in class. As you discuss the answers to these questions, draw students' attention to the numerators and the denominators. Help students to see that when you add fractions with like denominators, you add the numerators but the denominator does not change. This is because the size of the fractional part does not change, only the number of pieces you are concerned with.

To solve ***Question 1***, students use their eighths strips. They should begin with $\frac{5}{8}$ of the strip showing and then subtract $\frac{3}{8}$ of the strip. They show subtraction by folding back $\frac{3}{8}$ of the strip. Students will end with $\frac{2}{8}$ of their strips showing. Their number sentences should read: $\frac{5}{8} - \frac{3}{8} = \frac{2}{8}$.

Both ***Questions 2*** and ***3*** reinforce the concept that when the numerator and the denominator are the same number, the fraction indicates one whole. In ***Question 2***, students will use their fourths strips to add $\frac{1}{4}$ and $\frac{3}{4}$. The number sentence should read: $\frac{1}{4} + \frac{3}{4} = \frac{4}{4}$ or $\frac{1}{4} + \frac{3}{4} = 1$ whole.

To solve ***Question 3***, students will begin with their twelfths strips. Students should begin with the whole strip and then fold back $\frac{5}{12}$ of the strip to show subtraction. They will end up with $\frac{7}{12}$ of the strip. The number sentence is $\frac{12}{12} - \frac{5}{12} = \frac{7}{12}$ or $1 - \frac{5}{12} = \frac{7}{12}$.

Students use their sixths strips to solve ***Question 4***. For the first part of this question, begin with $\frac{5}{6}$ of the strip showing. Fold back $\frac{2}{6}$ of the strip. Students will be left with $\frac{3}{6}$ of the strip. The number sentence should read: $\frac{5}{6} - \frac{2}{6} = \frac{3}{6}$. For the second part of the question, students start with $\frac{3}{6}$ of their strip. They then fold back $\frac{1}{6}$ of the strip. They will be left with $\frac{2}{6}$ of the strip showing. The number sentence is $\frac{3}{6} - \frac{1}{6} = \frac{2}{6}$. ***Question 4C*** asks students to use their fraction strips to find an equivalent fraction to $\frac{2}{6}$. They will need to compare their sixths strip to other fraction strips to find fractions ($\frac{1}{3}$, $\frac{3}{9}$, $\frac{4}{12}$) that are equivalent to $\frac{2}{6}$.

Students will need to work with a partner to solve ***Questions 5–7***. In ***Question 5***, each student will need to use his or her tenths strip. After adding $\frac{8}{10}$ and $\frac{8}{10}$, students should find that Ming's total trip was $\frac{16}{10}$ miles. Some students may recognize this as $1\frac{6}{10}$ miles; however, not all students will make this connection. Changing improper fractions to mixed numbers will be studied in fifth grade. It is not necessary that students do this at this time. The possible number sentences for ***Question 5*** are $\frac{8}{10} + \frac{8}{10} = 1\frac{6}{10}$ or $\frac{8}{10} + \frac{8}{10} = \frac{16}{10}$.

To complete ***Question 6***, each pair of students will need to use both of their fourths strips. After adding $\frac{3}{4}$ and $\frac{2}{4}$, students should find that Irma must wait $\frac{5}{4}$ hours before going outside. Students may recognize this as $1\frac{1}{4}$ hours. The possible number sentences for ***Question 6*** are: $\frac{3}{4} + \frac{2}{4} = \frac{5}{4}$ or $\frac{3}{4} + \frac{2}{4} = 1\frac{1}{4}$. Either sentence is acceptable.

Suggestions for Teaching the Lesson

Math Facts

DPP Bit G provides review of division facts. Task H uses multiplication facts to review prime numbers, composite numbers, and prime factorization.

Homework and Practice

Assign homework ***Questions 1–7*** on the *Adding and Subtracting with Fraction Strips* Activity Pages. Students will need to take home their fraction strips to solve these problems.

Assessment

- Homework ***Questions 1–7*** on the *Adding and Subtracting with Fraction Strips* Activity Pages can be used to assess students' abilities to add and subtract fractions with like denominators using manipulatives.
- Use the *Observational Assessment Record* to note students' progress with addition and subtraction of fractions with like denominators.

Journal Prompt

Michael completed the following problem: $\frac{3}{8} + \frac{2}{8} = \frac{5}{16}$. Is his answer correct? Why or why not?

Homework

Use your fraction strips to complete the following problems. Write a number sentence for each problem.

1. Grace needed $\frac{5}{8}$ of a yard of ribbon to decorate the outside edge of a picture frame. She needed another $\frac{3}{8}$ of a yard of ribbon to decorate the inside edge of her frame. How much ribbon did she need to finish the frame?
2. A. On Monday, John ate $\frac{1}{5}$ of a box of cookies. On Tuesday, he ate another $\frac{2}{5}$ of the cookies. What fraction of the cookies did he eat altogether?
   B. What fraction of the cookies is left?
3. A. Jerome lives $\frac{7}{10}$ of a mile from school. If he has already walked $\frac{3}{10}$ of a mile, how much farther does he have to go before he gets to school?
   B. Use your fraction strips to find another fraction that is equal to your answer.
4. Tanya and Nila used their fraction strips to add fractions. Look at their work. Write a number sentence to show what they did.

Tanya's Strip

+

Nila's Strip

5. Use your fraction strips to complete the following number sentences.
   A. $\frac{1}{12} + \frac{4}{12} =$ B. $\frac{7}{10} - \frac{5}{10} =$ C. $\frac{5}{8} + \frac{3}{8} =$
6. Maya and Jerome used their fraction strips to show the following addition problem. Write a number sentence for their work.

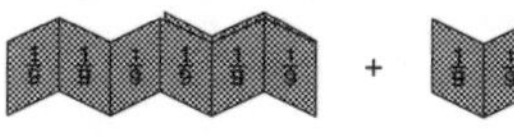
Maya's Strip

+

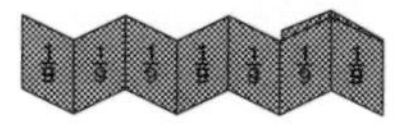
Jerome's Strip

7. Michael and his brother shared a pizza.
   A. Michael ate $\frac{2}{8}$ of a whole pizza. How much pizza was left?
   B. His brother ate another $\frac{3}{8}$ of the whole pizza. How much pizza was left?
   C. How much pizza did Michael and his brother eat altogether?

Adding and Subtracting with Fraction Strips SG · Grade 4 · Unit 12 · Lesson 2 335

***Student Guide* - Page 335**

Daily Practice and Problems: Task for Lesson 2

H. Task: Prime Factors (URG p. 15)  

1. Which of the following are prime numbers?

   53 54 57 67 96 103

2. For the composite numbers, use factor trees to factor them into a product of primes. You may use a calculator to help.

AT A GLANCE

Math Facts and Daily Practice and Problems

DPP Bit G provides practice with division facts and Task H provides practice with prime factorization.

Developing the Activity

1. Read the vignette on the *Adding and Subtracting with Fraction Strips* Activity Pages in the *Student Guide.*
2. Review Keenya's and Jacob's solutions to the problems presented.
3. Students use their fraction strips to complete ***Questions 1–7*** in pairs. Discuss students' strategies.

Homework

Assign homework ***Questions 1–7*** in the *Student Guide.* Students will need their fraction strips.

Assessment

Use the *Observational Assessment Record* to note students' progress adding and subtracting fractions with like denominators using manipulatives.

Notes:

Student Guide

Questions 1–7 (SG p. 334)

1. *$\frac{2}{8}$ yd
2. *$\frac{4}{4}$ or 1 cup
3. *$\frac{7}{12}$
4. A. *$\frac{3}{6}$ pie
   B. $\frac{2}{6}$ pie
   C. $\frac{1}{3}, \frac{3}{9}, \frac{4}{12}$
5. *$\frac{16}{10}$ or $1\frac{6}{10}$ miles (Accept either the improper fraction or mixed number.)
6. *$\frac{5}{4}$ hours or $1\frac{1}{4}$ hours
7. A. $\frac{5}{8}$
   B. $\frac{12}{10}$ or $1\frac{2}{10}$
   C. $\frac{6}{6}$ or 1
   D. $\frac{7}{12}$
   E. $\frac{2}{5}$
   F. $\frac{4}{8}$

Homework (SG p. 335)

Questions 1–7

1. $\frac{8}{8}$ or 1 yard
2. A. $\frac{3}{5}$ of a box
   B. $\frac{2}{5}$ of a box
3. A. $\frac{4}{10}$ of a mile
   B. $\frac{2}{5}$
4. $\frac{9}{12} + \frac{7}{12} = \frac{16}{12}$ or $1\frac{4}{12}$ (Accept either the improper fraction or mixed number.)
5. A. $\frac{5}{12}$
   B. $\frac{2}{10}$
   C. $\frac{8}{8}$ or 1
6. $\frac{6}{9} + \frac{7}{9} = \frac{13}{9}$ or $1\frac{4}{9}$
7. A. $\frac{6}{8}$ pizza
   B. $\frac{3}{8}$ pizza
   C. $\frac{5}{8}$ pizza

*Answers and/or discussion are included in the Lesson Guide.
**Answers for all the Home Practice in the *Discovery Assignment Book* are at the end of the unit.

Daily Practice and Problems: Bit for Lesson 3

I. Decimals from Pictures (URG p. 16) **N**

Write a decimal for the shaded part of each picture. The flat is one whole.

1. 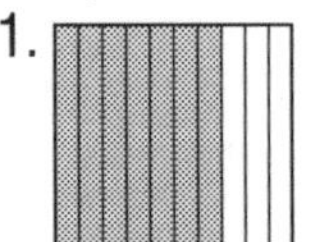
2. 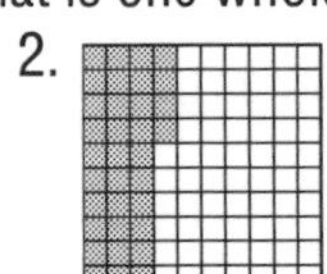
3. 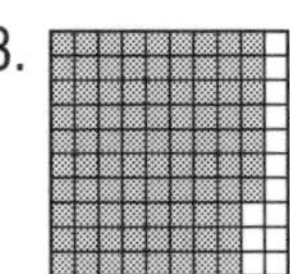
4. 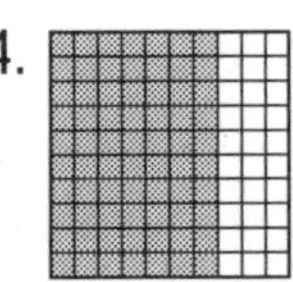

The DPP Task is on page 47. Suggestions for using the DPPs are on page 47.

LESSON GUIDE 

Comparing Fractions

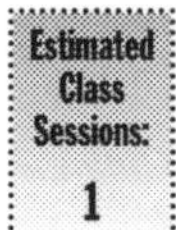

Students organize their fraction strips in a chart and then use the chart to compare and order fractions according to size.

Key Content

- Comparing fractions using manipulatives.

Key Vocabulary

benchmark

Materials List

Print Materials for Students

		Math Facts and Daily Practice and Problems	Activity	Homework
Student Book	Student Guide		*Comparing Fractions* Pages 336–337	*Comparing Fractions* Homework Section Page 338
Teacher Resource	Unit Resource Guide	DPP Items I–J Page 16 (available on Teacher Resource CD)		

available on Teacher Resource CD

All Transparency Masters, Blackline Masters, and Assessment Blackline Masters in the Unit Resource Guide are on the Teacher Resource CD.

Supplies for Each Student

set of fraction strips from Lesson 1
blank sheet of paper
glue

Materials for the Teacher

Fraction Strips for the Teacher Blackline Masters (Unit Resource Guide) Pages 36–37
Fraction Chart Transparency Master (Unit Resource Guide) Page 49
Observational Assessment Record (Unit Resource Guide, Pages 9–10 and Teacher Resource CD)

Before the Activity

Using the *Fraction Strips for the Teacher* Blackline Master, cut out, color, and mount one set of fraction strips on a chart as shown in Figure 11. Display this chart in the classroom for use during this lesson.

Developing the Activity

Pose the following question:

- *Jerome has $\frac{2}{3}$ yard of ribbon and Shannon has $\frac{1}{2}$ yard of ribbon. Who has more ribbon?*

Have students share the strategies they used. Suggest using fraction strips to help answer this question.

Tell students that they are going to create a visual tool so that they can easily compare the sizes of different fractions. Each student will need a complete set of fraction strips and a blank sheet of paper on which to mount them. To make the chart, students should first experiment with organizing the strips so that they build charts that will be useful for comparing fractions. Ask two or three students:

- *How did you decide to order your fraction strips?*
- *How will the order help you compare fractions?*

For example, students may decide to organize their charts from top to bottom in descending order from the largest-sized piece to the smallest-sized piece. An example of this is shown in Figure 11. Other students may choose to organize their charts by placing the strips in groups of related fractions as shown in Figure 12.

Students will then glue their strips to blank sheets of paper in the order they choose. The only guidelines that must be followed by all students are:

- Students must be prepared to explain the order in which they place the strips. They must be able to show how they will use it.
- Strips should be placed so that the long edges line up one against the other.
- Glue strips down so that they are touching each other. This makes it easier to compare fractions.
- The left and right edges of all of the strips must be lined up.

1 Whole											
$\frac{1}{2}$	$\frac{1}{2}$										
$\frac{1}{3}$	$\frac{1}{3}$	$\frac{1}{3}$									
$\frac{1}{4}$	$\frac{1}{4}$	$\frac{1}{4}$	$\frac{1}{4}$								
$\frac{1}{5}$	$\frac{1}{5}$	$\frac{1}{5}$	$\frac{1}{5}$	$\frac{1}{5}$							
$\frac{1}{6}$	$\frac{1}{6}$	$\frac{1}{6}$	$\frac{1}{6}$	$\frac{1}{6}$	$\frac{1}{6}$						
$\frac{1}{8}$	$\frac{1}{8}$	$\frac{1}{8}$	$\frac{1}{8}$	$\frac{1}{8}$	$\frac{1}{8}$	$\frac{1}{8}$	$\frac{1}{8}$				
$\frac{1}{9}$	$\frac{1}{9}$	$\frac{1}{9}$	$\frac{1}{9}$	$\frac{1}{9}$	$\frac{1}{9}$	$\frac{1}{9}$	$\frac{1}{9}$	$\frac{1}{9}$			
$\frac{1}{10}$	$\frac{1}{10}$	$\frac{1}{10}$	$\frac{1}{10}$	$\frac{1}{10}$	$\frac{1}{10}$	$\frac{1}{10}$	$\frac{1}{10}$	$\frac{1}{10}$	$\frac{1}{10}$		
$\frac{1}{12}$	$\frac{1}{12}$	$\frac{1}{12}$	$\frac{1}{12}$	$\frac{1}{12}$	$\frac{1}{12}$	$\frac{1}{12}$	$\frac{1}{12}$	$\frac{1}{12}$	$\frac{1}{12}$	$\frac{1}{12}$	$\frac{1}{12}$

Figure 11: *A fraction chart*

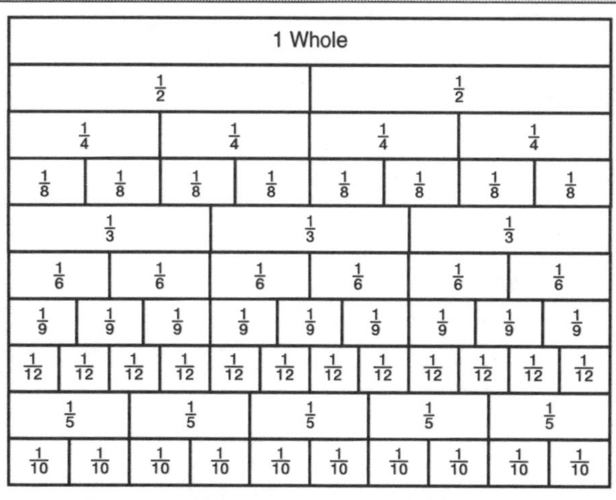

Figure 12: *Another way to organize a fraction chart*

TIMS Tip

The ten fraction strips will fit on an $8\frac{1}{2} \times 11$ inch sheet of paper, if they are placed horizontally as shown in Figures 11 and 12. In order to help students line up their strips so they are straight, suggest that students align their first strip along the top edge of their papers. They can also match either the right or left edge (short edge) of their strips with the corresponding edges of their papers.

Comparing Fractions

Fraction Chart

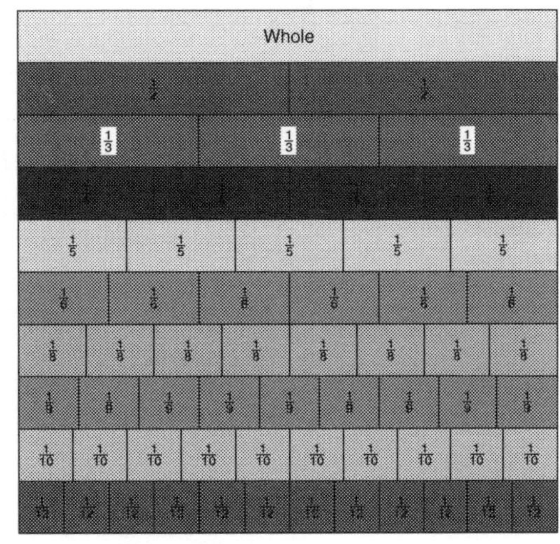

336 SG · Grade 4 · Unit 12 · Lesson 3 Comparing Fractions

***Student Guide* - Page 336**

Use your fraction strip chart to complete the following questions.

1. Grace and her little sister each ordered a personal pizza for dinner. Grace ate $\frac{3}{4}$ of her pizza. Her little sister ate $\frac{1}{2}$ of her pizza. Who ate more pizza?
2. Roberto walks $\frac{7}{10}$ of a mile to get to school. Keenya walks $\frac{2}{3}$ of a mile to get to school. Who lives closer to the school, Keenya or Roberto?

3. Use your chart to find the fractions that are equal to $\frac{1}{2}$ on the chart. Make a list of these fractions.
4. Use your fraction chart to compare the following pairs of fractions. Write number sentences using <, >, or =. For example, $\frac{1}{2} > \frac{1}{3}$.
   A. $\frac{1}{4}, \frac{1}{2}$ B. $\frac{2}{3}, \frac{1}{2}$ C. $\frac{1}{2}, \frac{2}{5}$
   D. $\frac{1}{2}, \frac{3}{6}$ E. $\frac{5}{12}, \frac{1}{2}$ F. $\frac{6}{9}, \frac{1}{2}$
5. Use $\frac{1}{2}$ as a benchmark or your fraction chart to compare the following pairs of fractions. Write number sentences using <, >, or =.
   A. $\frac{3}{4}, \frac{1}{3}$ B. $\frac{2}{5}, \frac{7}{10}$ C. $\frac{5}{8}, \frac{5}{12}$
   D. $\frac{2}{4}, \frac{6}{12}$ E. $\frac{3}{9}, \frac{2}{3}$ F. $\frac{3}{5}, \frac{1}{4}$
6. Use your fraction chart to put the following fractions in order from smallest to largest.
   A. $\frac{1}{3}, \frac{1}{6}, \frac{1}{2}$ B. $\frac{3}{5}, \frac{3}{4}, \frac{3}{12}$ C. $\frac{2}{10}, \frac{2}{4}, \frac{2}{9}$
7. Look at your answers for Question 6. Use them to help you answer this question: If two or more fractions have the same numerator, how can you tell which one is smallest?
8. Put the following fractions in order from smallest to largest.
   A. $\frac{4}{6}, \frac{1}{3}, \frac{1}{2}$ B. $\frac{7}{9}, \frac{4}{10}, \frac{3}{4}$ C. $\frac{3}{5}, \frac{5}{6}, \frac{1}{4}$ D. $\frac{5}{6}, \frac{5}{12}, \frac{5}{8}$
9. Explain your strategies for Questions 8A and 8D.

Comparing Fractions SG · Grade 4 · Unit 12 · Lesson 3 337

***Student Guide* - Page 337**

Once students have completed their charts, they can use them to complete the *Comparing Fractions* Activity Pages in the *Student Guide.* A copy of the fraction chart has been included in the *Student Guide,* but this chart is smaller than the students' charts. Students need to keep their fraction charts for use as a reference in later lessons of this unit. After students have completed the *Comparing Fractions* Activity Pages, provide an opportunity for students to share their work.

Discuss ***Question 4*** together noting that $\frac{1}{2}$ appears in ***Questions 4A–4F***. Point out that $\frac{1}{2}$ is a good benchmark to use when comparing the sizes of different fractions. For example, if you are comparing $\frac{1}{4}$ to $\frac{3}{5}$, you know that $\frac{1}{4}$ is smaller than $\frac{1}{2}$ and $\frac{3}{5}$ is a little larger than $\frac{1}{2}$. Therefore, $\frac{1}{4}$ is smaller than $\frac{3}{5}$. Students can practice using $\frac{1}{2}$ as a benchmark in ***Question 5*** since each pair of fractions students compare includes one fraction that is equal to or less than $\frac{1}{2}$ and one fraction that is greater than or equal to $\frac{1}{2}$.

TIMS Tip

If students are not familiar with the symbols for less than (<) and greater than (>), model this before students answer ***Question 4.***

Question 7 asks students how to order fractions if they all have the same numerator. Students should see that when all of the fractions have the same numerator, you can order them according to their denominators, the larger the denominator the smaller the fraction. Reinforce this concept by having students refer back to their charts.

For ***Questions 8–9,*** encourage students to use a second strategy to check their answers. For example, students can use $\frac{1}{2}$ as a benchmark to order the fractions in ***Question 8A,*** then check their work using their fraction charts.

Journal Prompt

Explain why $\frac{1}{2}$ is a good benchmark to use when comparing the sizes of different fractions.

Suggestions for Teaching the Lesson

Homework and Practice

- Homework ***Questions 1–8*** on the *Comparing Fractions* Activity Pages can be assigned as homework. Students may use their fraction charts to complete this work.
- DPP Bit I provides practice translating between representations of decimals (diagrams and symbols). Task J provides practice with multidigit multiplication and rounding.

Assessment

- Observe your students as they make and use their fraction charts. Note how well students compare and order fractions. Record your observations on the *Observational Assessment Record.*
- ***Questions 6–8*** of the Homework section on the *Comparing Fractions* Activity Pages can also be used to assess students' abilities to compare and order fractions.

Daily Practice and Problems: Task for Lesson 3

J. Task: More Multiplication N
(URG p. 16)

1. Solve the following using a paper-and-pencil method.

   A. $239 \times 7 =$ B. $3729 \times 3 =$

   C. $2390 \times 2 =$ D. $79 \times 23 =$

2. Find at least two ways to round each of the answers to Questions 1A through 1D.

Homework

Complete the following questions. You may use your fraction chart to help you.

1. Find all the fractions equal to $\frac{1}{4}$ on your chart. Make a list of these fractions.
2. Jackie needs $\frac{5}{8}$ of a yard of fabric for a pillow. Luis needs $\frac{3}{4}$ of a yard of fabric for a banner. Who needs more fabric, Jackie or Luis?
3. Jessie's mom brought a pie to the potluck dinner. It was cut into 6 pieces. Romesh's dad also brought a pie, but it was cut into 12 pieces. At the end of the night $\frac{1}{6}$ of Jessie's pie was left and $\frac{3}{12}$ of Romesh's pie was left. If the pies were the same size, who had more left-over pie, Jessie's mom or Romesh's dad?

4. Nila practiced her flute for $\frac{1}{2}$ hour on Monday, $\frac{3}{4}$ hour on Tuesday, and $\frac{1}{3}$ hour on Wednesday.
   A. On which day did she practice the longest period of time?
   B. On which day did she practice the shortest period of time?
5. Use your fraction chart to compare the following pairs of fractions. Write a number sentence for each one using <, >, or =.
   A. $\frac{3}{10}, \frac{1}{2}$ B. $\frac{4}{8}, \frac{1}{2}$ C. $\frac{1}{2}, \frac{2}{12}$
6. Use $\frac{1}{2}$ as a benchmark or your fraction chart to compare the following pairs of fractions. Write a number sentence for each one using <, >, or =.
   A. $1, \frac{1}{10}$ B. $\frac{6}{9}, \frac{5}{12}$ C. $\frac{3}{8}, \frac{3}{5}$
7. Use your fraction chart to put the following fractions in order from smallest to largest.
   A. $\frac{4}{8}, \frac{4}{6}, \frac{4}{10}$ B. $\frac{3}{5}, \frac{3}{10}, \frac{3}{8}$ C. $\frac{4}{8}, \frac{4}{12}, \frac{4}{6}$
   D. If two fractions have the same numerator, how can you tell which one is smaller?
8. Put the following fractions in order from smallest to largest. Be prepared to explain your strategies.
   A. $\frac{7}{12}, \frac{1}{3}, \frac{3}{8}$ B. $\frac{3}{5}, \frac{5}{12}, \frac{1}{2}$ C. $\frac{2}{3}, \frac{3}{4}, \frac{1}{6}$
   D. $\frac{1}{5}, \frac{1}{4}, \frac{1}{6}$ E. $\frac{7}{12}, \frac{1}{12}, \frac{5}{12}$ F. $\frac{1}{2}, \frac{3}{4}, \frac{2}{9}$

338 SG • Grade 4 • Unit 12 • Lesson 3 Comparing Fractions

***Student Guide* - Page 338**

AT A GLANCE

Math Facts and Daily Practice and Problems

DPP Bit I provides practice with decimals. DPP Task J provides practice with multidigit multiplication.

Developing the Activity

1. Using the *Fraction Strips for the Teacher* Blackline Masters, cut out, color, and mount one set of fraction strips on a chart for demonstration.
2. Students discuss the opening question given in the Lesson Guide and share strategies for finding a solution.
3. Students make a fraction chart with their fraction strips by gluing the strips on a piece of paper.
4. Students use their charts to complete ***Questions 1–8*** on the *Comparing Fractions* Activity Pages in the *Student Guide.*
5. Discuss solutions for ***Questions 1–8.***
6. Students keep their charts to use as a reference in later lessons in this unit.

Homework

Assign homework ***Questions 1–8*** in the *Student Guide.*

Assessment

Use the *Observational Assessment Record* to note students' abilities to order fractions.

Notes:

Fraction Chart

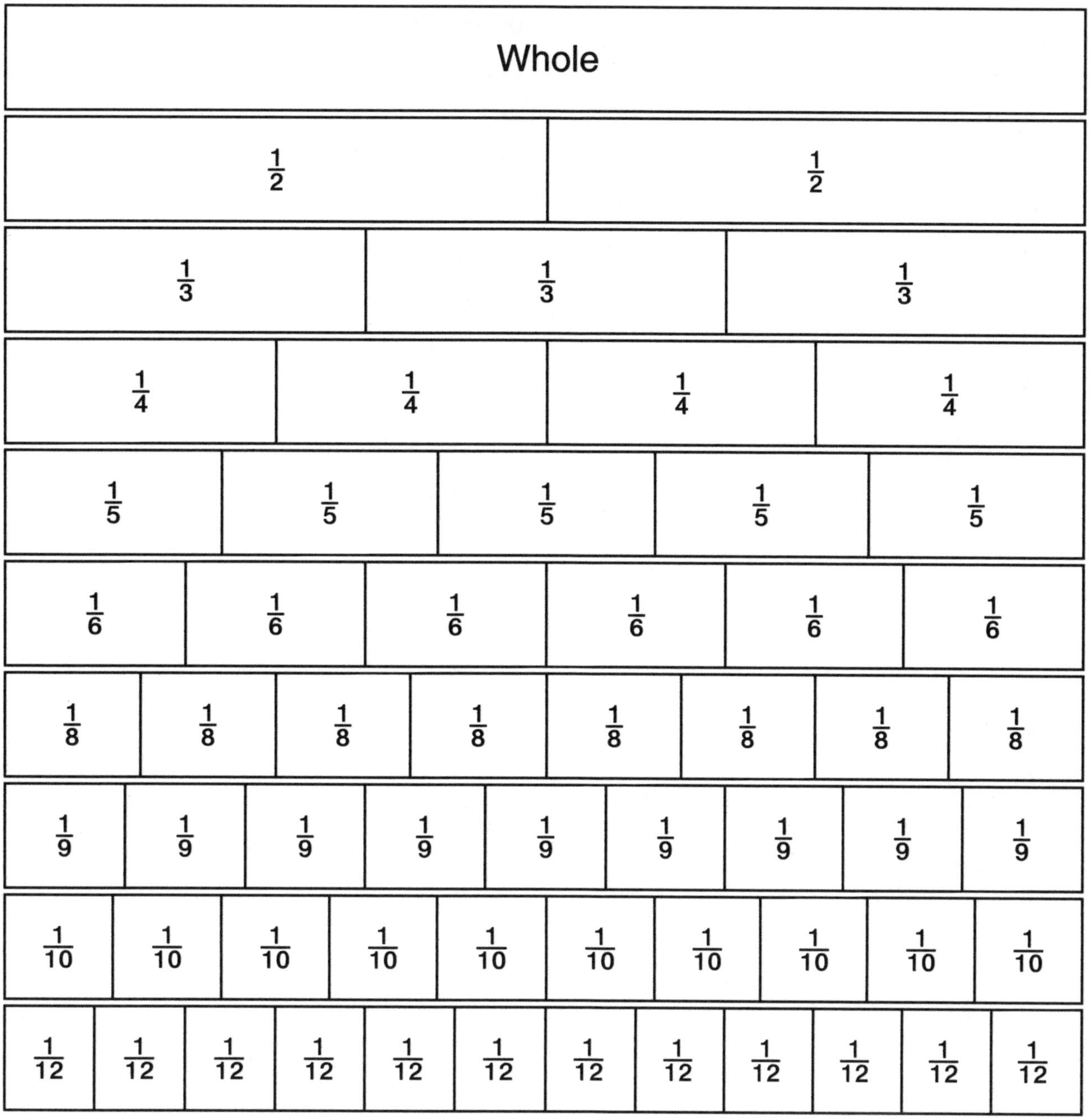

Whole											
$\frac{1}{2}$	$\frac{1}{2}$										
$\frac{1}{3}$	$\frac{1}{3}$	$\frac{1}{3}$									
$\frac{1}{4}$	$\frac{1}{4}$	$\frac{1}{4}$	$\frac{1}{4}$								
$\frac{1}{5}$	$\frac{1}{5}$	$\frac{1}{5}$	$\frac{1}{5}$	$\frac{1}{5}$							
$\frac{1}{6}$	$\frac{1}{6}$	$\frac{1}{6}$	$\frac{1}{6}$	$\frac{1}{6}$	$\frac{1}{6}$						
$\frac{1}{8}$	$\frac{1}{8}$	$\frac{1}{8}$	$\frac{1}{8}$	$\frac{1}{8}$	$\frac{1}{8}$	$\frac{1}{8}$	$\frac{1}{8}$				
$\frac{1}{9}$	$\frac{1}{9}$	$\frac{1}{9}$	$\frac{1}{9}$	$\frac{1}{9}$	$\frac{1}{9}$	$\frac{1}{9}$	$\frac{1}{9}$	$\frac{1}{9}$			
$\frac{1}{10}$	$\frac{1}{10}$	$\frac{1}{10}$	$\frac{1}{10}$	$\frac{1}{10}$	$\frac{1}{10}$	$\frac{1}{10}$	$\frac{1}{10}$	$\frac{1}{10}$	$\frac{1}{10}$		
$\frac{1}{12}$	$\frac{1}{12}$	$\frac{1}{12}$	$\frac{1}{12}$	$\frac{1}{12}$	$\frac{1}{12}$	$\frac{1}{12}$	$\frac{1}{12}$	$\frac{1}{12}$	$\frac{1}{12}$	$\frac{1}{12}$	$\frac{1}{12}$

Student Guide

Questions 1–9 (SG p. 337)

1. Grace
2. Keenya
3. $\frac{2}{4}, \frac{3}{6}, \frac{4}{8}, \frac{5}{10}, \frac{6}{12}$
4. A. *$\frac{1}{4} < \frac{1}{2}$
   B. $\frac{2}{3} > \frac{1}{2}$
   C. $\frac{1}{2} > \frac{2}{5}$
   D. $\frac{1}{2} = \frac{3}{6}$
   E. $\frac{5}{12} < \frac{1}{2}$
   F. $\frac{6}{9} > \frac{1}{2}$
5. A. *$\frac{3}{4} > \frac{1}{3}$
   B. $\frac{2}{5} < \frac{7}{10}$
   C. $\frac{5}{8} > \frac{5}{12}$
   D. $\frac{2}{4} = \frac{6}{12}$
   E. $\frac{3}{9} < \frac{2}{3}$
   F. $\frac{3}{5} > \frac{1}{4}$
6. A. $\frac{1}{6}, \frac{1}{3}, \frac{1}{2}$
   B. $\frac{3}{12}, \frac{3}{5}, \frac{3}{4}$
   C. $\frac{2}{10}, \frac{2}{9}, \frac{2}{4}$
7. *When the numerators are the same, the fraction with the largest denominator is the smallest fraction.
8. A. *$\frac{1}{3}, \frac{1}{2}, \frac{4}{6}$
   B. $\frac{4}{10}, \frac{3}{4}, \frac{7}{9}$
   C. $\frac{1}{4}, \frac{3}{5}, \frac{5}{6}$
   D. $\frac{5}{12}, \frac{5}{8}, \frac{5}{6}$
9. *Possible strategies for ***Question 8A:***
   Use a fraction chart. Or, use $\frac{1}{2}$ as a benchmark. $\frac{1}{3}$ is less than $\frac{1}{2}$ and $\frac{4}{6}$ is greater than $\frac{1}{2}$, so $\frac{1}{3} < \frac{1}{2} < \frac{4}{6}$.

   Possible strategies for ***Question 8D:***
   Use a fraction chart. Or, since all the fractions have the same numerator, the fractions with the larger denominators are the smaller fractions so that $\frac{5}{12} < \frac{5}{8} < \frac{5}{6}$.

Homework (SG p. 338)

Questions 1–8

1. $\frac{2}{8}, \frac{3}{12}$
2. Luis
3. Romesh's dad
4. A. Tuesday
   B. Wednesday
5. A. $\frac{3}{10} < \frac{1}{2}$
   B. $\frac{4}{8} = \frac{1}{2}$
   C. $\frac{1}{2} > \frac{2}{12}$
6. A. $1 > \frac{1}{10}$
   B. $\frac{6}{9} > \frac{5}{12}$
   C. $\frac{3}{8} < \frac{3}{5}$
7. A. $\frac{4}{10}, \frac{4}{8}, \frac{4}{6}$
   B. $\frac{3}{10}, \frac{3}{8}, \frac{3}{5}$
   C. $\frac{4}{12}, \frac{4}{8}, \frac{4}{6}$
   D. When the numerators are the same, the fraction with the larger denominator is the smaller fraction.
8. A. $\frac{1}{3}, \frac{3}{8}, \frac{7}{12}$
   B. $\frac{5}{12}, \frac{1}{2}, \frac{3}{5}$
   C. $\frac{1}{6}, \frac{2}{3}, \frac{3}{4}$
   D. $\frac{1}{6}, \frac{1}{5}, \frac{1}{4}$
   E. $\frac{1}{12}, \frac{5}{12}, \frac{7}{12}$
   F. $\frac{2}{9}, \frac{1}{2}, \frac{3}{4}$

***Answers and/or discussion are included in the Lesson Guide.**
****Answers for all the Home Practice in the *Discovery Assignment Book* are at the end of the unit.**

LESSON GUIDE 

Frabble Game and Bubble Sort

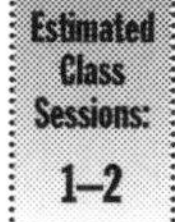

Students use a deck of fraction cards to complete two activities. First, students play a game in small groups in which they order fractions according to size by strategically placing cards on the table. Then, in an activity called Bubble Sort, each student holds a fraction card and stands in line. Then, following some simple rules, students rearrange themselves so that the cards are in decreasing order.

Key Content

- Comparing and ordering fractions.
- Finding equivalent fractions.

OPTIONAL LESSON

There are no Daily Practice and Problems items for this lesson.

Materials List

Print Materials for Students

Student Books		Optional Game
	Student Guide	*Frabble Game and Bubble Sort* Pages 339–342 and Fraction Chart from *Comparing Fractions* Page 336
	Discovery Assignment Book	*Standard Frabble Cards* Pages 203–205, 1 set per group, *Wild Cards for Frabble* Page 207, 2 cards per player, and *Challenge Frabble Cards* Page 209 (optional)

available on Teacher Resource CD

All Transparency Masters, Blackline Masters, and Assessment Blackline Masters in the Unit Resource Guide are on the Teacher Resource CD.

Supplies for Each Student

scissors
envelopes, optional
fraction chart made in Lesson 3

Materials for the Teacher

Transparencies of *Standard Frabble Cards* Game Pages (Discovery Assignment Book) Pages 203–205, optional
Fraction chart created by the teacher in Lesson 3 or *Fraction Chart* Transparency Master (Unit Resource Guide) Page 49
Observational Assessment Record (Unit Resource Guide, Pages 9–10 and Teacher Resource CD)

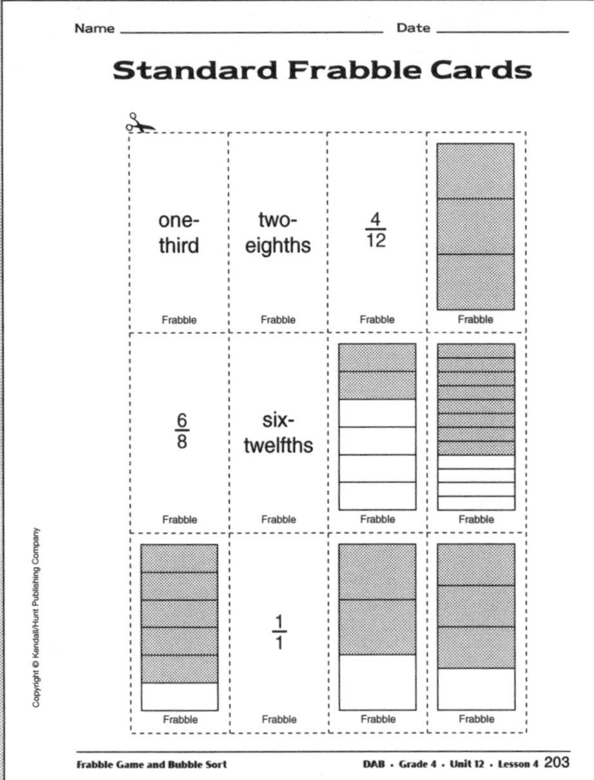

Name ______________________ Date ____________

Standard Frabble Cards

one-third Frabble	two-eighths Frabble	$\frac{4}{12}$ Frabble	Frabble
$\frac{6}{8}$ Frabble	six-twelfths Frabble	Frabble	Frabble
Frabble	$\frac{1}{1}$ Frabble	Frabble	Frabble

***Discovery Assignment Book* - Page 203**

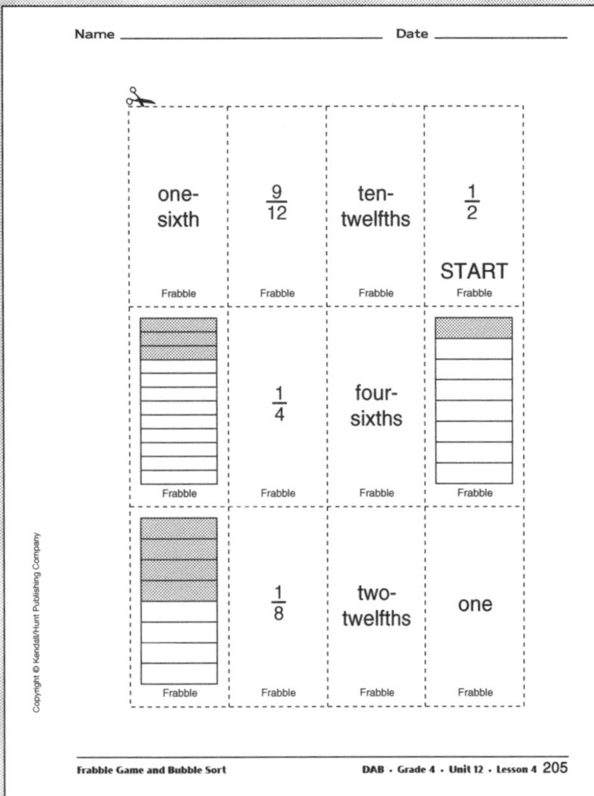

Name ______________________ Date ____________

one-sixth Frabble	$\frac{9}{12}$ Frabble	ten-twelfths Frabble	$\frac{1}{2}$ START Frabble
Frabble	$\frac{1}{4}$ Frabble	four-sixths Frabble	Frabble
Frabble	$\frac{1}{8}$ Frabble	two-twelfths Frabble	one Frabble

***Discovery Assignment Book* - Page 205**

Before the Game

This game can be played in groups of two, three, or four players. Each group needs one deck of 24 *Standard Frabble Cards* from the *Discovery Assignment Book.* Each group can cut out a set of cards before they begin to play or you may make decks of cards and laminate them so that the cards will last longer. Each student will also need two wild cards in order to play this game.

> **TIMS Tip**
>
> Have students store their cards in an envelope when they are not being used. Students should also include eight wild cards in their decks so they can play the game at home.

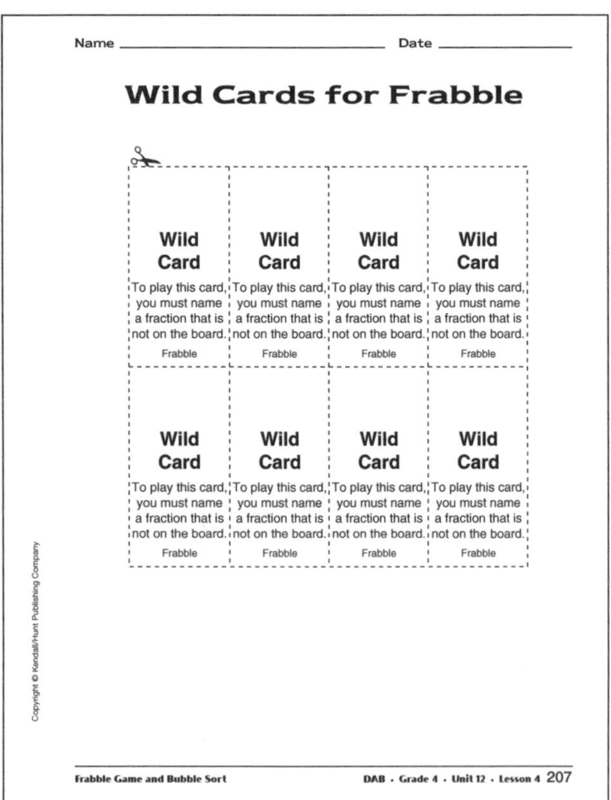

Name ______________________ Date ____________

Wild Cards for Frabble

Wild Card To play this card, you must name a fraction that is not on the board. Frabble	**Wild Card** To play this card, you must name a fraction that is not on the board. Frabble	**Wild Card** To play this card, you must name a fraction that is not on the board. Frabble	**Wild Card** To play this card, you must name a fraction that is not on the board. Frabble
Wild Card To play this card, you must name a fraction that is not on the board. Frabble	**Wild Card** To play this card, you must name a fraction that is not on the board. Frabble	**Wild Card** To play this card, you must name a fraction that is not on the board. Frabble	**Wild Card** To play this card, you must name a fraction that is not on the board. Frabble

***Discovery Assignment Book* - Page 207**

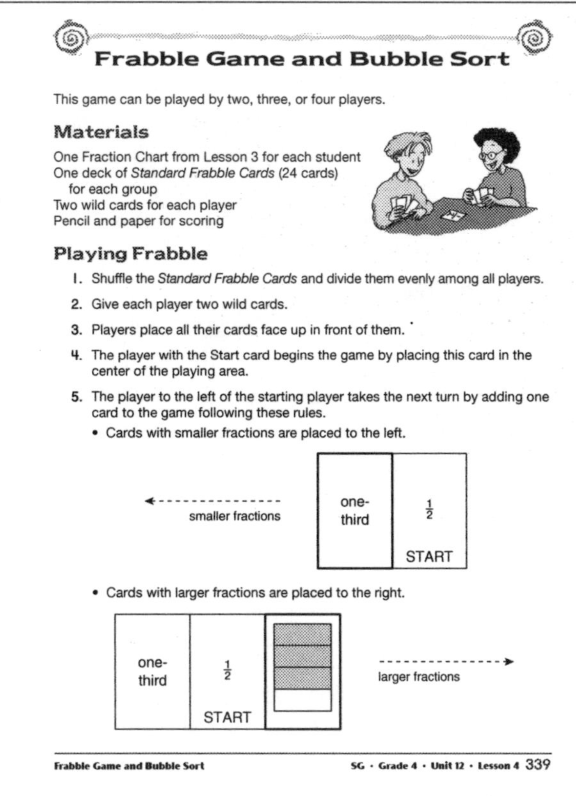

Frabble Game and Bubble Sort

This game can be played by two, three, or four players.

Materials

One Fraction Chart from Lesson 3 for each student
One deck of *Standard Frabble Cards* (24 cards) for each group
Two wild cards for each player
Pencil and paper for scoring

Playing Frabble

1. Shuffle the *Standard Frabble Cards* and divide them evenly among all players.
2. Give each player two wild cards.
3. Players place all their cards face up in front of them.
4. The player with the Start card begins the game by placing this card in the center of the playing area.
5. The player to the left of the starting player takes the next turn by adding one card to the game following these rules.
   - Cards with smaller fractions are placed to the left.

   - Cards with larger fractions are placed to the right.

***Student Guide* - Page 339**

- Cards with equal fractions are placed above or below.

$\frac{6}{8}$ | one-third | $\frac{1}{2}$ START | one-third | $\frac{1}{2}$ START | $\frac{3}{6}$

or

- You can place a wild card at any time. To place a wild card, you must give the card a name that is not already on the board. For example, a wild card named $\frac{2}{6}$ can be placed below the one-third card.

one-third | $\frac{1}{2}$ START

Wild Card To play this card, you must name a fraction that is not on the board. Frabble | $\frac{3}{6}$

- You may not move any card that has already been played. For example, you may not move the $\frac{3}{4}$ card over in order to place a $\frac{2}{3}$ card between the $\frac{1}{2}$ and the $\frac{3}{4}$ card in the example shown above.

***Student Guide* - Page 340**

Developing the Game

Part 1. Playing *Frabble*

The rules of the game are explained on the *Frabble Game and Bubble Sort* Game Pages in the *Student Guide.* Discuss the rules using the illustrations in the text or demonstrate the rules by playing the game on the overhead projector using cards made from transparencies of the *Standard Frabble Cards.*

As students play the game, they will need to decide if one fraction is less than, greater than, or equivalent to other fractions. To help them order fractions, each student should have a fraction chart available. Students may use the fraction chart they made or the Fraction Chart on the *Comparing Fractions* Activity Pages in the *Student Guide* for Lesson 3.

After students have played the game with the standard deck of 24 fraction cards and have become familiar with both the rules and the strategies of the game, they can make the game more interesting by adding 12 challenge cards. These cards can be found on the *Challenge Frabble Cards* Game Page in the *Discovery Assignment Book.* The challenge cards add fractions with denominators of fifths and tenths to the standard deck which is limited to fractions with denominators of halves, thirds, fourths, sixths, eighths, and twelfths.

6. If you do not have a card that can be placed on the board, you lose a turn. The game ends when no player can take a turn. The player with the most points wins the game.

Scoring

One player is chosen to write down each person's points at the end of each turn. Points are scored by these rules:

- The player who places the "Start" card earns one point for placing one card on the board.
- Each player earns:
  1 point for each card played
  1 point for each card connected to the new card in the row
  1 point for each card on the board that has a fraction equal to the card played

Example 1: The player who places the "one" card earns four points. The player gets one point for playing the card and three points for the three cards connected to the new card in the same row.

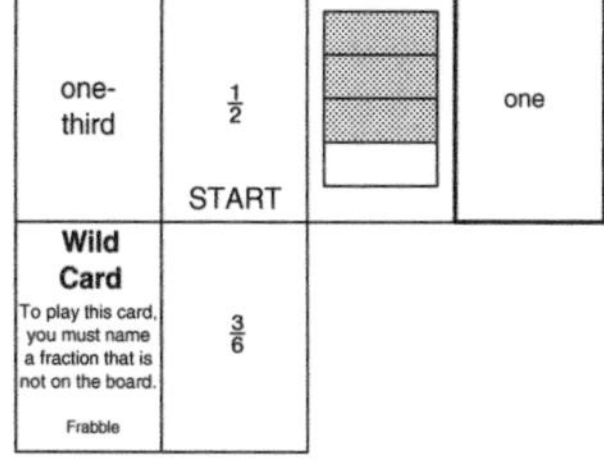

***Student Guide* - Page 341**

Example 2: The player who adds the $\frac{1}{1}$ card earns two points: One point for playing the card ($\frac{1}{1}$) and one point for the equal fraction (one).

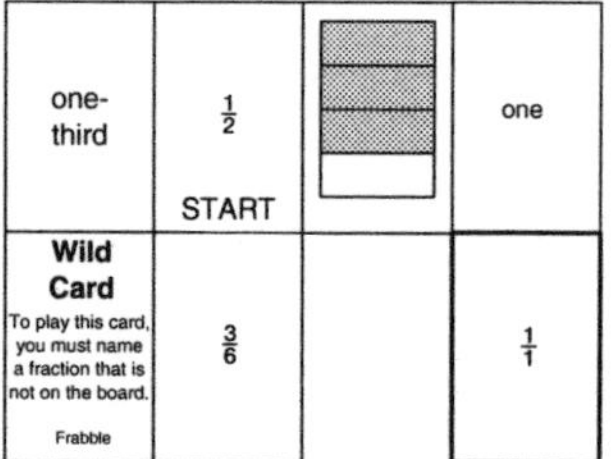

Example 3: The player who adds the $\frac{6}{8}$ card earns a total of five points: One point for the card added ($\frac{6}{8}$); three points for the cards connected in the row (wild card, $\frac{3}{6}$, and $\frac{1}{1}$); and one point for the equal fraction (picture of $\frac{3}{4}$).

one-third	$\frac{1}{2}$ START	[picture]	one
Wild Card To play this card, you must name a fraction that is not on the board. Frabble	$\frac{3}{6}$	$\frac{6}{8}$	$\frac{1}{1}$

***Student Guide* - Page 342**

Name ______________________ Date ____________

Challenge Frabble Cards

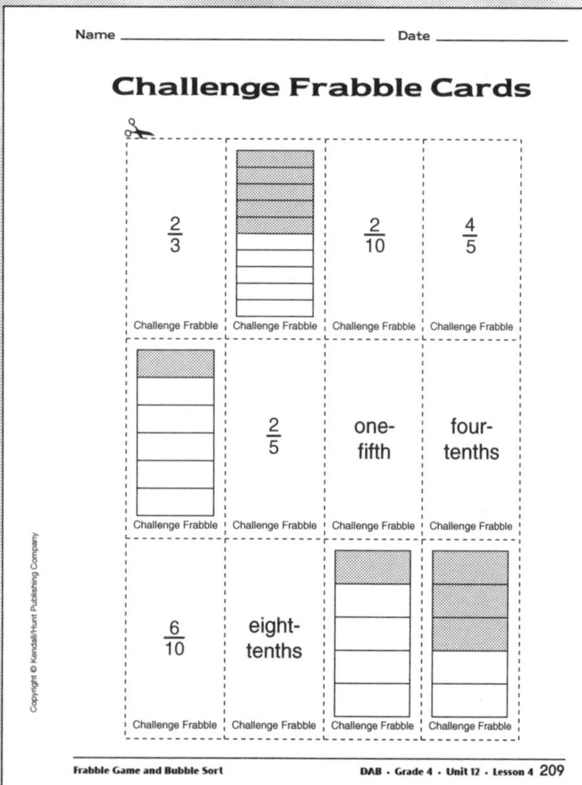

***Discovery Assignment Book* - Page 209**

TIMS Tip

Each group of students playing a game needs a scorekeeper. You can make up a rule to determine which one of the players will serve as the scorekeeper first, such as "the child in each group whose name comes first (or last) alphabetically" or "the student on the east side of the table."

Part 2. Bubble Sort

Randomly pass out a *Frabble* card to each student and then ask the class to stand in one line. Tell students that they will follow a procedure called Bubble Sort that will sort the cards from largest to smallest. Designate the head of the line as the home of the largest number and the other end of the line as the home of the smallest number. The object of the sort is for the largest fractions to "bubble up" to the head of the line.

TIMS Tip

The bubble sort can be demonstrated to the class with five students before the whole class begins the sort.

To bubble sort:

- Ask the first two students at the head of the line to compare the fractions on their cards. If the smaller fraction is at the head of the line, then the students switch places. If the larger fraction is already at the head of the line or if the fractions are equivalent, the students stay in their original places.
- Then, the second and third students in line compare their fractions, switching places so that the larger fraction moves toward the head of the line.
- Continue with the students currently standing in the third and fourth places and then with the remaining students in the line until all adjacent pairs have compared and ordered their two fractions.

Note that the students change places, they do not trade cards, and that they may only switch places with a student who is standing to the left or right of them.

Once the end of the line is reached, ask the students to read the fractions on their cards out loud. Ask

- *Are all the fractions in order?*

After one pass through the line, it is not likely that the fractions will be in order, so the process is repeated. Once students understand the procedure, speed up the ordering process by having adjacent pairs of students compare their fractions simultaneously and switch places as necessary. Remind students that they may only switch places with a student standing to the left or right of them.

Continue until no more switches can be made. Then, ask students to read off the numbers as a final check to see that the fractions are in order.

Suggestions for Teaching the Lesson

Homework and Practice

Students play *Frabble* with their families. Each student will need to take home a deck of *Frabble* cards, six wild cards, and his or her *Student Guide.*

Assessment

- As students play the game, look for students' abilities to order fractions correctly. Record your observations on the *Observational Assessment Record.*
- Choose five of the *Frabble* cards (such as 1, $\frac{1}{8}$, $\frac{1}{2}$, a picture of $\frac{1}{6}$, and four-sixths) and ask students to place them in order on their desks. Students can write the order of the cards on a sheet of paper or you can make a visual check. Record students' abilities to compare and order fractions on the *Observational Assessment Record.*

Extension

Use the *Frabble* cards to play Frabble War. This is a game for two players. Each student begins with half of the deck placed in a pile face down in front of him or her. Each player turns over the top card from his or her pile. Whoever has the greater fraction showing wins the two cards. If the two fractions are equivalent, then each player turns over another card. Whoever has the greater fraction wins all four cards. If there is another tie, then players turn over two more cards, continuing the process until the tie is broken. The player with the larger fraction wins all the cards in the "war." Students may play the cards they win. Play for 10 minutes or until one player runs out of cards. The player with the most cards at the end of the game is the winner.

Challenge students to make up a card game using the *Frabble* cards.

Content Note

Bubble Sort. The bubble sort demonstrates an algorithm computer programmers sometimes use to order numbers or words in a list. The name comes from the image of bubbles in water bubbling up to the surface. There are faster sorting schemes, but this one works well in a classroom. You may wish to start the sort by designating one student (or yourself) as the computer. During the first or second pass through the line, the computer looks at each pair of adjacent fractions and decides if students holding the cards should switch places or not. This will go slowly and students will soon want to make the comparisons simultaneously.

AT A GLANCE

Before the Game

Make decks of *Standard Frabble Cards* from the *Discovery Assignment Book.* Each group will need one deck. Each student will also need two wild cards. Prepare Challenge cards to be added to the deck after students are comfortable with the rules.

Part 1. Playing *Frabble*

1. Discuss the rules of the game using the illustrations in the *Student Guide* or transparencies of *Standard Frabble Cards.*
2. Students play the game in groups of 2, 3, or 4 using one deck of *Standard Frabble Cards* and keeping score with pencil and paper.
3. When students are familiar with the rules and strategies of the game, groups can add the *Challenge Frabble Cards* to the deck.

Part 2. Bubble Sort

1. Each student stands in a line holding a *Frabble* card.
2. The head of the line is designated the home for the largest fraction on the cards and the other end of the line is the home for the smallest fraction.
3. Students compare the fractions on their cards with the fractions on the cards of the students standing on either side of them. If a student has the larger fraction, he or she trades places with the person with the smaller fraction, moving toward the head of the line. Students continue comparing fractions and trading places with the students immediately next to them when appropriate until all of the fractions are in order from largest to smallest.

Homework

Students play *Frabble* at home. They should take home a deck of *Frabble* cards, six wild cards, and their *Student Guides.*

Assessment

Use the *Observational Assessment Record* to note students' abilities to compare and order fractions.

Notes:

LESSON GUIDE 

Equivalent Fractions

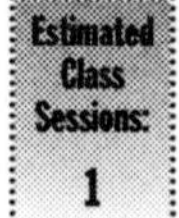

Students find equivalent fractions using their fraction charts from Lesson 3, write number sentences to represent the equivalent fractions, and look for patterns in the number sentences. They use these patterns to write an equivalent fraction for a given fraction.

Key Content

- Finding equivalent fractions.

Key Vocabulary

equivalent fractions

Daily Practice and Problems: Bit for Lesson 5

K. More Division Fact Practice (URG p. 17) 

Find the number n that makes each sentence true.

A. $54 \div n = 9$

B. $720 \div n = 90$

C. $n \times 400 = 36,000$

D. $70 \times n = 63,000$

E. $90 \times n = 450$

F. $n \div 9 = 300$

The DPP Task is on page 61. Suggestions for using the DPPs are on page 61.

Materials List

Print Materials for Students

		Math Facts and Daily Practice and Problems	Activity	Homework	Written Assessment
Student Books	Student Guide		*Equivalent Fractions* Pages 343–344 and Fraction Chart from *Comparing Fractions* Page 336	*Equivalent Fractions* Homework Section Pages 344–345	
Student Books	Discovery Assignment Book				Home Practice Part 3 Page 194
Teacher Resources	Facts Resource Guide (CD)	DPP Items 12K & 12L			
Teacher Resources	Unit Resource Guide	DPP Items K–L Page 17 (CD)			

(CD) *available on Teacher Resource CD*

All Transparency Masters, Blackline Masters, and Assessment Blackline Masters in the Unit Resource Guide are on the Teacher Resource CD.

Supplies for Each Student

fraction chart made in Lesson 3 *Comparing Fractions*

Materials for the Teacher

Observational Assessment Record (Unit Resource Guide, Pages 9–10 and Teacher Resource CD)

Developing the Activity

The first part of this lesson is a teacher-led activity in which students look at equivalent fractions using their fraction charts from Lesson 3. Students look for patterns and use these patterns to find equivalent fractions that are not shown on their charts.

Begin this lesson by putting the fraction $\frac{1}{2}$ on the board or on a blank overhead transparency. Ask students to look at their fraction charts and find all of the fractions that are equivalent to $\frac{1}{2}$. List these on the board as shown in Figure 13. Explain that fractions with the same value are called **equivalent fractions.**

$$\frac{1}{2} = \frac{2}{4} = \frac{3}{6} = \frac{4}{8} = \frac{5}{10} = \frac{6}{12}$$

Figure 13: *Fractions that are equivalent to $\frac{1}{2}$*

Use the discussion prompts provided to explore these equivalent fractions:

- *Compare the denominators of each of these fractions. What do you notice?* (Students should see that the denominators are all even numbers and therefore all multiples of two.)
- *Compare the numerator and the denominator in each fraction. What do you see?* (When a fraction is equivalent to $\frac{1}{2}$ the numerator is half the value of the denominator.)
- *Is $\frac{20}{40}$ equivalent to $\frac{1}{2}$?* (Since 40 is a multiple of 2 and since 20 is half of 40, then $\frac{20}{40} = \frac{1}{2}$.)
- *Suggest other fractions that are equivalent to $\frac{1}{2}$.* (Evaluate each student suggestion, adding those that are appropriate to the list of equivalent fractions.)

Write the following number sentences on the board: $\frac{1}{2} = \frac{2}{4}$; $\frac{1}{2} = \frac{4}{8}$; $\frac{1}{2} = \frac{5}{10}$; $\frac{1}{2} = \frac{6}{12}$; $\frac{1}{2} = \frac{20}{40}$, and some of the fractions suggested by the students. Ask:

- *Look for a pattern in these number sentences by first comparing the numerators of the fractions in each sentence and then the denominators.*

Students may express the patterns in many ways, but they should see that if you multiply (or divide) both the numerator and the denominator of a fraction by the same number the result will be an equivalent fraction. Figure 14 shows this pattern.

$$\frac{1}{2} = \frac{1 \times 5}{2 \times 5} = \frac{5}{10} \qquad \frac{6}{12} = \frac{6 \div 6}{12 \div 6} = \frac{1}{2}$$

Figure 14: *Equivalent fractions*

Continue this lesson by asking students to use their fraction charts to suggest number sentences for those fractions that are equivalent to $\frac{3}{4}$, $\frac{1}{3}$, and $\frac{2}{5}$. Write these on the board or overhead as shown in Figure 15. Using the pattern found earlier, ask:

- *What number should I multiply both the numerator and denominator by to find the equivalent fraction?*

$$\frac{3}{4} = \frac{3 \times \square}{4 \times \square} = \frac{6}{8} \qquad \frac{3}{4} = \frac{3 \times \square}{4 \times \square} = \frac{9}{12}$$

$$\frac{1}{3} = \frac{1 \times \square}{3 \times \square} = \frac{2}{6} \qquad \frac{1}{3} = \frac{1 \times \square}{3 \times \square} = \frac{4}{12}$$

$$\frac{2}{5} = \frac{2 \times \square}{5 \times \square} = \frac{4}{10}$$

Figure 15: *Equivalent fractions*

Once students have completed this task, ask them to suggest other fractions that are equivalent to $\frac{3}{4}$, $\frac{1}{3}$, and $\frac{2}{5}$. Add these fractions to the board by writing the appropriate number sentences. For example, students may suggest the following number sentences for $\frac{3}{4}$: $\frac{3}{4} = \frac{30}{40}$ and $\frac{3}{4} = \frac{300}{400}$. As students suggest number sentences, ask them to explain how they found the equivalent fractions.

Once students are comfortable using multiplication to find equivalent fractions, put the following number sentences on the board:

$$\frac{?}{3} = \frac{4}{6} \qquad \frac{10}{12} = \frac{?}{6} \qquad \frac{6}{10} = \frac{3}{?} \qquad \frac{?}{4} = \frac{2}{8}$$

Ask students to find the missing numerators and denominators. Students should share the strategies that they use. Students may suggest using multiplication as a strategy. For example, to find the missing number in the sentence $\frac{?}{3} = \frac{4}{6}$, students may say: "Since you multiply 3 by 2 in order to get the denominator of 6, what number would you multiply by 2 in order to get the numerator of 4? Since 2 times 2 equals 4, the missing numerator is 2." Other students may suggest using division as a strategy. For example, in the number sentence $\frac{10}{12} = \frac{?}{6}$, they may say, "Since you divide 12 by 2 in order to get 6, you must also divide 10 by 2. This gives a numerator of 5."

Equivalent Fractions

Irma wants to bake some cookies. Her recipe calls for $\frac{3}{4}$ cup sugar. Irma can only find a $\frac{1}{8}$-cup measure. She needs to know how many eighths of a cup of sugar is the same as $\frac{3}{4}$ cup. She knows that two $\frac{1}{8}$-cup measures hold the same amount of sugar as a $\frac{1}{4}$-cup measure. She knows that she needs enough sugar to fill three $\frac{1}{4}$-cup measures because she needs $\frac{3}{4}$ cup. She reasons that she must fill the $\frac{1}{8}$ cup twice as many times, or six times. Irma also remembers what she learned in math class: If you multiply (or divide) the numerator and the denominator of a fraction by the same number, you will get an equal or equivalent fraction. **Equivalent fractions** are fractions that have the same value.

To solve this problem Irma can use this number sentence: $\frac{3}{4} = \frac{?}{8}$.

1. A. Help Irma solve this problem. Think of a strategy she can use.
   B. Irma knows that $4 \times 2 = 8$. Since she multiplied 4 times 2 to find the new denominator, she also must multiply 3 times 2 in order to find the missing numerator. Complete this number sentence for Irma: $\frac{3}{4} = \frac{?}{8}$.

2. Romesh is helping his father pack a box of key chains for a fundraiser. The box holds $\frac{1}{2}$ pound of merchandise. Each key chain weighs $\frac{1}{16}$ of a pound. Romesh must decide how many key chains he can fit in the box.
   A. Help Romesh by completing this number sentence: $\frac{1}{2} = \frac{?}{16}$.
   B. How many key chains can Romesh pack in the box?

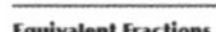

SG • Grade 4 • Unit 12 • Lesson 5 343

Student Guide - Page 343

3. A. Use your fraction chart to find three fractions that are equivalent to $\frac{3}{9}$. Write number sentences to record the equivalent fractions.
   B. Find three other fractions that are equivalent to $\frac{3}{9}$. Write number sentences to record the equivalent fractions.
   C. Explain the strategy you used to find the equivalent fractions.
4. Complete the number sentence: $\frac{4}{8} = \frac{?}{12}$. Explain how you know.
5. A. Use your fraction chart to find a fraction that is equivalent to $\frac{3}{5}$. Write a number sentence to record the equivalent fractions.
   B. Find three other fractions that are equivalent to $\frac{3}{5}$. Write number sentences to record the equivalent fractions.
   C. Explain the strategy you used to find the equivalent fractions.
6. Complete the number sentences below. Use your fraction chart.

   A. $\frac{3}{4} = \frac{?}{8}$ B. $\frac{1}{2} = \frac{?}{10}$ C. $\frac{2}{3} = \frac{?}{9}$ D. $\frac{6}{9} = \frac{?}{12}$

   E. $\frac{1}{2} = \frac{4}{?}$ F. $\frac{6}{10} = \frac{?}{5}$ G. $\frac{8}{12} = \frac{2}{?}$ H. $\frac{3}{12} = \frac{?}{8}$

Homework

1. Maya wrote number sentences to show fractions that are equivalent to $\frac{1}{2}$. She forgot to write in some of the numerators and denominators. Write Maya's number sentences filling in the missing numbers to make each fraction equivalent to $\frac{1}{2}$.

   A. $\frac{1}{2} = \frac{3}{?}$ B. $\frac{1}{2} = \frac{?}{18}$ C. $\frac{1}{2} = \frac{12}{?}$

   D. $\frac{1}{2} = \frac{?}{60}$ E. $\frac{1}{2} = \frac{50}{?}$ F. $\frac{1}{2} = \frac{?}{?}$
2. Write 5 fractions equivalent to $\frac{2}{3}$.
3. Romesh is packing a box filled with plastic cars for his father. The box holds $\frac{3}{4}$ pound of merchandise. Each plastic car weighs $\frac{1}{16}$ pound.

   A. Complete this number sentence to help Romesh decide how many sixteenths of a pound is equivalent to $\frac{3}{4}$ pound. $\frac{3}{4} = \frac{?}{16}$.
   B. How many plastic cars can Romesh pack in the box?
   C. What is another name for $\frac{1}{16}$ of a pound?

344 SG • Grade 4 • Unit 12 • Lesson 5 Equivalent Fractions

Student Guide - Page 344

Continue this lesson by having students use the *Equivalent Fractions* Activity Pages in the *Student Guide.* The short vignette reviews the concepts completed in class. After reviewing the vignette, students can complete ***Questions 1–6.*** These questions can be completed with a partner or students can work independently and then check their work with another student. Provide an opportunity for students to share their answers and strategies.

Discuss ***Questions 3–4.*** For ***Question 3A*** students use their fraction charts to find that $\frac{1}{3}$, $\frac{2}{6}$, and $\frac{4}{12}$ are equivalent to $\frac{3}{9}$. Write $\frac{3}{9} = \frac{2}{6}$ on the board. Point out that nine is not a multiple of six. Ask:

- *How do you know that $\frac{3}{9}$ is equal to $\frac{2}{6}$?* (The fraction strips for $\frac{3}{9}$ and $\frac{2}{6}$ are the same length. $\frac{3}{9}$ and $\frac{2}{6}$ are both equal to $\frac{1}{3}$.)
- *How do you know that $\frac{3}{9}$ is equal to $\frac{4}{12}$?* (The fraction strips for $\frac{3}{9}$ and $\frac{4}{12}$ are the same length. $\frac{3}{9}$ and $\frac{4}{12}$ are both equal to $\frac{1}{3}$.)

Question 4 asks students to complete the number sentence $\frac{6}{12} = \frac{?}{8}$. Since students cannot multiply numerator and denominator by the same whole number to find an equivalent fraction, they must use another strategy. Students can use their fraction charts to show that the length of the $\frac{6}{12}$ fraction strip is the same length as the $\frac{4}{8}$ fraction strip. Or, they can use the fact that $\frac{6}{12}$ and $\frac{4}{8}$ are both equal to $\frac{1}{2}$.

> **Content Note**
>
> **Equivalent Fractions.** In mathematics, two fractions that have the same value are considered equivalent fractions. At this level of mathematics, we do not distinguish between the words equal and equivalent. Therefore, it is acceptable for students to use either equal or equivalent when comparing two fractions that have the same value.

Suggestions for Teaching the Lesson

Math Facts

DPP items K and L provide practice with math facts using numbers with ending zeros.

Homework and Practice

Assign the Homework section of the *Equivalent Fractions* Activity Pages in the *Student Guide*. Students will need their fraction charts.

Assessment

- Use the *Observational Assessment Record* to note students' progress finding equivalent fractions.
- Use Part 3 of the Home Practice to assess students' abilities to order fractions and find equivalent fractions.

Answers for the Home Practice Part 3 can be found in the Answer Key at the end of this lesson and at the end of this unit.

Daily Practice and Problems: Task for Lesson 5

L. Task: Fact Practice (URG p. 17)

A. $30 \times 90 =$

B. $630 \div 70 =$

C. $360 \div 9 =$

D. $90 \times 80 =$

E. $2700 \div 9 =$

F. $9000 \times 90 =$

G. $54{,}000 \div 9 =$

H. $1800 \div 90 =$

I. $900 \times 0 =$

J. $900 \div 90 =$

4. Write 5 fractions equivalent to $\frac{2}{5}$.
5. Shannon wants to purchase $\frac{1}{3}$ yard of ribbon. There are 36 inches in a yard.
   A. Complete the following number sentence to help the clerk decide how many inches of ribbon she must cut: $\frac{1}{3} = \frac{?}{36}$.
   B. How many inches of ribbon should she cut?

6. Use the Fraction Chart to complete the number sentence: $\frac{6}{8} = \frac{?}{12}$.

Complete the following number sentences.

7. $\frac{1}{2} = \frac{?}{12}$ 8. $\frac{3}{4} = \frac{?}{16}$ 9. $\frac{4}{6} = \frac{?}{9}$

10. $\frac{3}{5} = \frac{?}{20}$ 11. $\frac{10}{16} = \frac{?}{8}$ 12. $\frac{8}{24} = \frac{?}{3}$

13. $\frac{10}{15} = \frac{?}{3}$ 14. $\frac{1}{5} = \frac{?}{100}$ 15. $\frac{1}{5} = \frac{?}{20}$

16. $\frac{75}{100} = \frac{?}{4}$ 17. $\frac{2}{4} = \frac{?}{6}$ 18. $\frac{20}{24} = \frac{5}{?}$

Use <, >, or = to write number sentences to compare the following pairs of numbers.

19. $\frac{5}{9}, \frac{1}{2}$ 20. $\frac{3}{4}, \frac{30}{40}$ 21. $\frac{72}{100}, \frac{7}{10}$

Equivalent Fractions SG · Grade 4 · Unit 12 · Lesson 5 345

***Student Guide* - Page 345**

Name ______________________ Date ______________

Part 3 Fraction Chart

Use the fraction chart you created in Lesson 3 or the Fraction Chart in your *Student Guide* in Lesson 3.

1. Order these fractions from smallest to largest.
   A. $\frac{2}{3}$ $\frac{1}{4}$ $\frac{5}{6}$ $\frac{3}{8}$ $\frac{2}{12}$ ______________________
   B. $\frac{3}{5}$ $\frac{1}{8}$ $\frac{4}{9}$ $\frac{1}{10}$ $\frac{1}{2}$ ______________________
2. Find one or two equivalent fractions for each of the following.
   A. $\frac{6}{8}$ B. $\frac{3}{9}$ C. $\frac{2}{3}$ D. $\frac{4}{10}$
   E. $\frac{3}{5}$ F. $\frac{3}{12}$ G. $\frac{6}{12}$ H. $\frac{1}{5}$
3. Complete the number sentences.
   A. $\frac{5}{6} = \frac{?}{12}$ B. $\frac{8}{10} = \frac{4}{?}$ C. $\frac{4}{5} = \frac{?}{20}$
4. Name a fraction smaller than each of the following.
   A. $\frac{1}{2}$ B. $\frac{1}{4}$ C. $\frac{3}{5}$ D. $\frac{7}{8}$
5. Name a fraction greater than each of the following. Do not name a fraction equivalent to 1.
   A. $\frac{1}{2}$ B. $\frac{3}{4}$ C. $\frac{1}{6}$ D. $\frac{9}{10}$

194 DAB · Grade 4 · Unit 12 EXPLORING FRACTIONS

***Discovery Assignment Book* - Page 194**

AT A GLANCE

Math Facts and Daily Practice and Problems

Use DPP items K and L to practice multiplication and division facts as students build number sense.

Developing the Activity

1. Ask students to use their fraction chart from Lesson 3 to find all of the fractions that are equivalent to $\frac{1}{2}$. List these on the board or overhead.
2. Ask students to compare the numerators and the denominators of the equivalent fractions in order to look for patterns.
3. Ask students to suggest other fractions that are equivalent to $\frac{1}{2}$.
4. Write number sentences on the board or overhead showing the equivalencies.
5. Students look for patterns in the number sentences.
6. Students use the patterns (multiplying or dividing the numerator and the denominator by the same number) to find fractions equivalent to $\frac{3}{4}$, $\frac{1}{3}$, and $\frac{2}{5}$.
7. Students use the patterns to complete number sentences involving equivalent fractions.
8. Students complete ***Questions 1–6*** on the *Equivalent Fractions* Activity Pages.
9. Discuss ***Questions 3*** and ***4*** as a class.

Homework

Assign the Homework section on the *Equivalent Fractions* Activity Pages in the *Student Guide*. Students will need their fraction charts to complete this assignment.

Assessment

1. Use the *Observational Assessment Record* to note students' abilities to find equivalent fractions.
2. Use Home Practice Part 3 as an assessment.

Notes:

Student Guide

Questions 1–6 (SG pp. 343–344)

1. **A.** Since multiplying the denominator (4) times 2 gives the denominator of the second fraction, multiply the numerator (3) by 2 to get the numerator (6) of the equivalent fraction.

   B. $\frac{3}{4} = \frac{6}{8}$
2. **A.** $\frac{1}{2} = \frac{8}{16}$

   B. 8 key chains
3. **A.** $\frac{3}{9} = \frac{1}{3} = \frac{2}{6} = \frac{4}{12}$

   B. $\frac{3}{9} = \frac{6}{18} = \frac{9}{27} = \frac{12}{36}$ (Answers will vary.)

   C. Multiply (or divide) numerator and denominator by the same number or use the Fraction Chart.
4. $\frac{4}{8} = \frac{6}{12}$. Explanations will vary. Possible explanations: The fraction strip for $\frac{4}{8}$ is the same length as the fraction strip for $\frac{6}{12}$. Or, I know that $\frac{4}{8}$ and $\frac{6}{12}$ both equal $\frac{1}{2}$.
5. **A.** $\frac{3}{5} = \frac{6}{10}$

   B. $\frac{3}{5} = \frac{9}{15} = \frac{12}{20} = \frac{15}{25}$ (Answers will vary.)

   C. Multiply numerator and denominator by the same number.
6. **A.** $\frac{3}{4} = \frac{6}{8}$

   B. $\frac{1}{2} = \frac{5}{10}$

   C. $\frac{2}{3} = \frac{6}{9}$

   D. $\frac{6}{9} = \frac{8}{12}$

   E. $\frac{1}{2} = \frac{4}{8}$

   F. $\frac{6}{10} = \frac{3}{5}$

   G. $\frac{8}{12} = \frac{2}{3}$

   H. $\frac{3}{12} = \frac{2}{8}$

Homework (SG pp. 344–345)

Questions 1–21

1. **A.** $\frac{1}{2} = \frac{3}{6}$

   B. $\frac{1}{2} = \frac{9}{18}$

   C. $\frac{1}{2} = \frac{12}{24}$

   D. $\frac{1}{2} = \frac{30}{60}$

   E. $\frac{1}{2} = \frac{50}{100}$

   F. Answers will vary.
2. $\frac{2}{3} = \frac{4}{6} = \frac{6}{9} = \frac{8}{12} = \frac{10}{15} = \frac{12}{18}$ (Answers will vary.)
3. **A.** $\frac{3}{4} = \frac{12}{16}$

   B. 12 cars

   C. an ounce
4. $\frac{2}{5} = \frac{4}{10} = \frac{6}{15} = \frac{8}{20} = \frac{10}{25} = \frac{12}{30}$ (Answers will vary.)
5. **A.** $\frac{1}{3} = \frac{12}{36}$

   B. 12 inches
6. $\frac{6}{8} = \frac{9}{12}$
7. $\frac{1}{2} = \frac{6}{12}$
8. $\frac{3}{4} = \frac{12}{16}$
9. $\frac{4}{6} = \frac{6}{9}$
10. $\frac{3}{5} = \frac{12}{20}$
11. $\frac{10}{16} = \frac{5}{8}$
12. $\frac{8}{24} = \frac{1}{3}$
13. $\frac{10}{15} = \frac{2}{3}$
14. $\frac{1}{5} = \frac{20}{100}$
15. $\frac{1}{5} = \frac{4}{20}$
16. $\frac{75}{100} = \frac{3}{4}$
17. $\frac{2}{4} = \frac{3}{6}$
18. $\frac{20}{24} = \frac{5}{6}$
19. $\frac{5}{9} > \frac{1}{2}$
20. $\frac{3}{4} = \frac{30}{40}$
21. $\frac{72}{100} > \frac{7}{10}$

*Answers and/or discussion are included in the Lesson Guide.

**Answers for all the Home Practice in the *Discovery Assignment Book* are at the end of the unit.

Discovery Assignment Book

**** Home Practice (DAB p. 194)**

Part 3. Fraction Chart

Questions 1–5

1. A. $\frac{2}{12}, \frac{1}{4}, \frac{3}{8}, \frac{2}{3}, \frac{5}{6}$

   B. $\frac{1}{10}, \frac{1}{8}, \frac{4}{9}, \frac{1}{2}, \frac{3}{5}$

2. Answers will vary. Students name 1 or 2 equivalent fractions for each letter.

   A. $\frac{3}{4}, \frac{9}{12}$

   B. $\frac{1}{3}, \frac{4}{12}$

   C. $\frac{4}{6}, \frac{6}{9}, \frac{8}{12}$

   D. $\frac{2}{5}$

   E. $\frac{6}{10}$

   F. $\frac{1}{4}, \frac{2}{8}$

   G. $\frac{1}{2}, \frac{2}{4}, \frac{3}{6}, \frac{4}{8}, \frac{5}{10}$

   H. $\frac{2}{10}$

3. A. $\frac{5}{6} = \frac{10}{12}$

   B. $\frac{8}{10} = \frac{4}{5}$

   C. $\frac{4}{5} = \frac{16}{20}$

4. Answers will vary.

5. Answers will vary.

*Answers and/or discussion are included in the Lesson Guide.

**Answers for all the Home Practice in the *Discovery Assignment Book* are at the end of the unit.

LESSON GUIDE 

Pattern Block Fractions

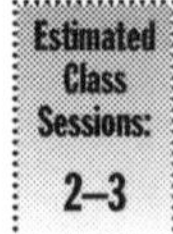

Students use pattern blocks to model fractions. They name fractions when a pattern block is defined as one whole and they identify the whole when a fraction is given. An optional activity, *What's 1?,* is included for students who have not had experiences using pattern blocks to represent fractions.

Key Content

- Representing fractions using pattern blocks.
- Finding a fraction for a given quantity when a unit whole is given.
- Identifying the unit whole when a fraction is given.
- Connecting mathematics to real-life situations.

Key Vocabulary

hexagon
rhombus
trapezoid

Daily Practice and Problems: Bits for Lesson 6

M. Fact Families for × and ÷ (URG p. 18) 

Solve the given fact. Then, name another fact that is in the same fact family.

A. $9 \times 8 =$

B. $54 \div 9 =$

C. $36 \div 4 =$

D. $9 \times 7 =$

O. Evenly Divisible (URG p. 19) 

Frank wants to buy stickers for his 6 friends who will be attending his birthday party. At the store, he sees four different collections of stickers.

One pad has 95 stickers.
One pad has 110 stickers.
One pad has 120 stickers.
One pad has 160 stickers.

Frank plans to buy one pad of stickers. If he wants to divide the stickers evenly among his 6 guests without any leftovers, which pad should he purchase? How did you decide?

DPP Task and Challenge are on page 70. Suggestions for using the DPPs are on page 70.

Curriculum Sequence

Before This Unit

Students used pattern blocks to represent fractions and investigate the concept of a whole in Grade 3 Unit 13.

After This Unit

Students will use pattern blocks in Grade 5 to represent fractions in Units 3, 5, and 12. They use them to develop paper-and-pencil procedures for addition, subtraction, and multiplication.

Materials List

Print Materials for Students

		Math Facts and Daily Practice and Problems	Activity	Homework
Student Books	Student Guide		*Pattern Block Fractions* Pages 346–349	*Pattern Block Fractions* Homework Section Page 349
	Discovery Assignment Book			Home Practice Parts 4 & 5 Page 195
Teacher Resources	Facts Resource Guide (CD)	DPP Items 12M & 12P		
	Unit Resource Guide	DPP Items M–P Pages 18–19 (CD)	*What's 1?* Pages 72–73, 1 per student (optional)	

(CD) *available on Teacher Resource CD*

All Transparency Masters, Blackline Masters, and Assessment Blackline Masters in the Unit Resource Guide are on the Teacher Resource CD.

Supplies for Each Student Pair

set of pattern blocks (at least 2 to 3 yellow hexagons, 6 red trapezoids, 10 blue rhombuses, 10 green triangles, 6 brown trapezoids)

Materials for the Teacher

Observational Assessment Record (Unit Resource Guide, Pages 9–10 and Teacher Resource CD)
overhead pattern blocks, optional

Before the Activity

In the third grade of the *Math Trailblazers* curriculum, students modeled fractions using pattern blocks. If your students have not had experience using pattern blocks or other manipulatives to represent fractions, have students complete the *What's 1?* Blackline Masters. These pages, taken from the third-grade materials, introduce students to the use of the yellow hexagons, red trapezoids, blue rhombuses, and green triangles to model fractions.

Question 1 asks students to compare sizes and determine the fractional relationships between the various pattern block pieces. These questions are a warmup for looking at fractional parts of a whole unit.

Questions 2–3 present problems in which students are given the whole and must find the fraction. Some questions also ask students to determine whether the fractions they identify are more than or less than one-half.

Questions 4–5 name a pattern block as a fraction, and students must then determine the unit whole. ***Question 6*** asks students to make drawings using pattern blocks. For example, ***Question 6B*** asks students to draw one whole if a green triangle is one-fifth. Note that there are many different shapes that can be drawn with five green triangles.

Questions 7–8 use a six-sided shape (hexagon) that is divided into tenths for one whole. See Figure 16. Ask students to identify the shape by name. Students are to determine both the fraction and decimal fraction for various given parts of the unit whole. For example, because ten greens cover the whole, one green is $\frac{1}{10}$ or 0.1. ***Question 7E*** asks students to write a fraction for 5 green triangles. Students may name either $\frac{1}{2}$ or $\frac{5}{10}$. Accept both answers and remind students that the two fractions name the same quantity and are equivalent. ***Questions 8B–8C*** ask students to write two different fractions for one blue rhombus. Since one blue rhombus equals two green triangles, the fractions are $\frac{2}{10}$ and $\frac{1}{5}$. ***Question 8D*** asks for the decimal fraction for one blue rhombus. Students should realize that $\frac{2}{10}$, $\frac{1}{5}$, and 0.2 all represent the same number.

Developing the Activity

Part 1. When Are Halves Different?

To begin the activity, students can read the short vignette on the *Pattern Block Fractions* Activity Pages in the *Student Guide.* Jacob and Jerome are discussing their data from the *Bouncing Ball* lab (see Unit 5). They imagine dropping a ball from the top of the Sears Tower in Chicago and from the top of the CN Tower in

TIMS Tip

Make the pattern blocks available to the students to explore in their free time several days before this lesson.

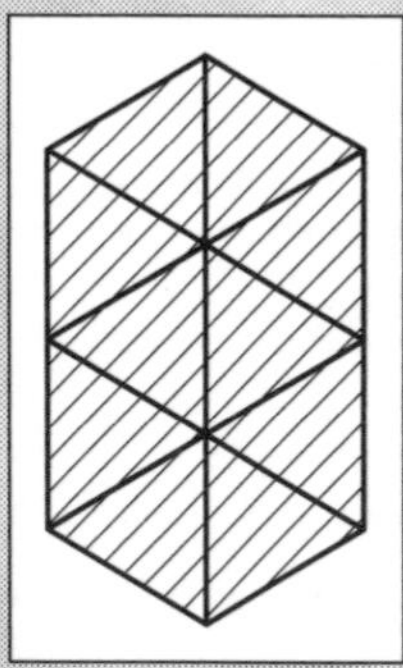

Figure 16: *A hexagon represents 1 whole.*

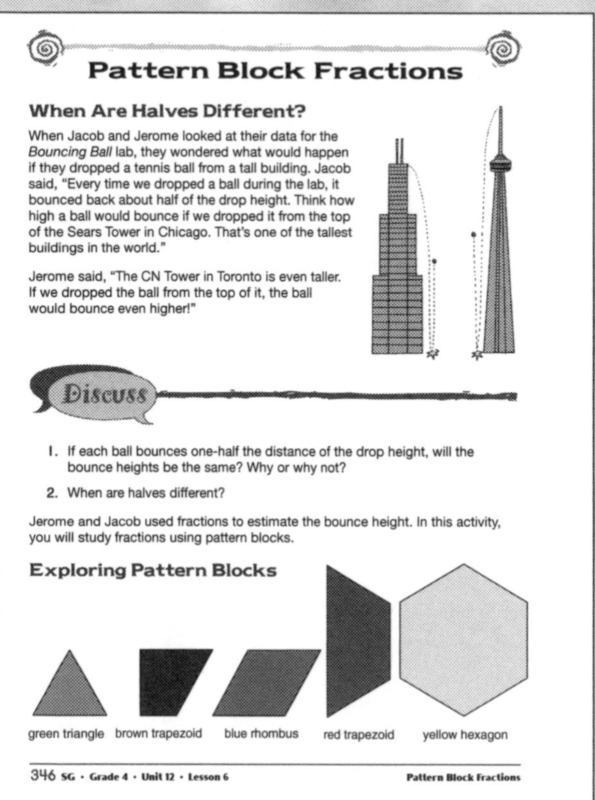

Pattern Block Fractions

When Are Halves Different?

When Jacob and Jerome looked at their data for the *Bouncing Ball* lab, they wondered what would happen if they dropped a tennis ball from a tall building. Jacob said, "Every time we dropped a ball during the lab, it bounced back about half of the drop height. Think how high a ball would bounce if we dropped it from the top of the Sears Tower in Chicago. That's one of the tallest buildings in the world."

Jerome said, "The CN Tower in Toronto is even taller. If we dropped the ball from the top of it, the ball would bounce even higher!"

Discuss

1. If each ball bounces one-half the distance of the drop height, will the bounce heights be the same? Why or why not?
2. When are halves different?

Jerome and Jacob used fractions to estimate the bounce height. In this activity, you will study fractions using pattern blocks.

Exploring Pattern Blocks

346 SG • Grade 4 • Unit 12 • Lesson 6 Pattern Block Fractions

Student Guide - Page 346

Use the blocks to help you answer the following questions:

3. How many brown trapezoids equal one yellow hexagon?
4. How many brown trapezoids equal one red trapezoid?
5. How many red trapezoids equal one yellow hexagon?
6. One brown trapezoid is (less than, greater than, or equal to) one red trapezoid.
7. How many brown trapezoids equal three red trapezoids?
8. One brown trapezoid is (less than, greater than, or equal to) one green triangle.
9. How many green triangles equal one yellow hexagon?
10. One yellow hexagon equals two brown trapezoids plus how many green triangles?
11. How many green triangles equal two brown trapezoids?
12. How many green triangles equal two blue rhombuses?
13. Two blue rhombuses are (less than, greater than, or equal to) one brown trapezoid.

Exploring Pattern Block Fractions

14. Each of these figures shows thirds using pattern blocks. Build these figures with pattern blocks. Place three blue rhombuses on a yellow hexagon. Place three green triangles on a red trapezoid.
    A. If the red trapezoid is one whole, which block shows $\frac{1}{3}$?
    B. If the blue rhombus is $\frac{1}{3}$, which block shows one whole?
    C. If the red trapezoid is one whole, show $\frac{2}{3}$.

Pattern Block Fractions SG • Grade 4 • Unit 12 • Lesson 6 347

***Student Guide* - Page 347**

15. A. Show halves using pattern blocks in as many ways as you can.
    B. If the yellow hexagon is one whole, which block shows $\frac{1}{2}$?
    C. If the green triangle is $\frac{1}{2}$, which block is one whole?
    D. If the brown trapezoid is $\frac{1}{2}$, which block is one whole?
16. A. If the yellow hexagon is one whole, which block shows $\frac{1}{4}$?
    B. If the yellow hexagon is one whole, show $\frac{3}{4}$.
    C. If the yellow hexagon is one whole, show $\frac{5}{4}$.
17. A. If the green triangle is $\frac{1}{6}$, which block is one whole?
    B. If the yellow hexagon is one whole, show $\frac{3}{6}$.
    C. If the yellow hexagon is one whole, show $\frac{5}{6}$.
18. If the red trapezoid is one whole, name each of the following fractions:
    A. one green triangle
    B. two green triangles
    C. one blue rhombus
    D. one brown trapezoid
    E. three brown trapezoids
    F. five green triangles

    one whole
19. If the yellow hexagon is one whole, name each of the following fractions:
    A. one red trapezoid
    B. one brown trapezoid
    C. two brown trapezoids
    D. one blue rhombus
    E. two green triangles
    F. two blue rhombuses
    G. three red trapezoids

    one whole

Fraction Sentences

For Questions 20–26, the yellow hexagon is one whole. The red trapezoid is $\frac{1}{2}$. We can show $\frac{1}{2}$ using brown blocks. Since 1 red trapezoid equals 2 brown trapezoids, then $\frac{1}{2} = \frac{2}{4}$ or $\frac{1}{2} = \frac{1}{4} + \frac{1}{4}$.

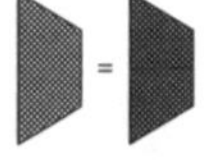

$\frac{1}{2} = \frac{2}{4}$
or
$\frac{1}{2} = \frac{1}{4} + \frac{1}{4}$

348 SG • Grade 4 • Unit 12 • Lesson 6 Pattern Block Fractions

***Student Guide* - Page 348**

Toronto. ***Question 1*** asks if each ball bounces $\frac{1}{2}$ the distance of the drop height, will they both bounce to the same height? Students will see that the bounce height for each ball will be different, but it may be more difficult for them to explain why. If the drop heights are different, halves of the drop heights will also be different. Halves are different when the unit wholes are different (***Question 2***). The size of a fraction depends on the size of the whole. Working on the questions in this lesson will help students understand this concept.

Part 2. Exploring Pattern Blocks

As mentioned above, in third grade, students used pattern blocks in their study of fractions. They used the yellow hexagons, red trapezoids, blue rhombuses, and green triangles. When the yellow hexagon is designated as the whole, students can work with halves, thirds, and sixths using these blocks. In this lesson, students add brown trapezoids. The brown trapezoid is one-fourth of the yellow hexagon. ***Questions 3–13*** guide students through an exploration of the relative sizes of the five kinds of pattern blocks. Figure 17 shows the brown trapezoid in relation to a yellow hexagon.

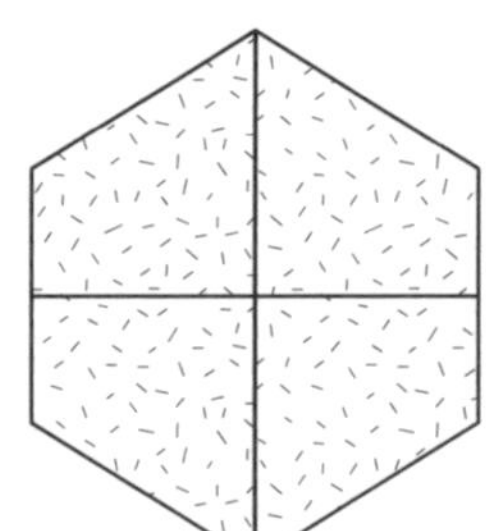

Figure 17: *A brown trapezoid is $\frac{1}{4}$ of the yellow hexagon.*

Part 3. Exploring Pattern Block Fractions

Questions 14–19 ask students to name fractions when the whole is given and name the whole when a fraction is given. For example, ***Question 14*** asks students to show thirds in different ways using pattern blocks. See Figure 18. They identify the green triangle as $\frac{1}{3}$ of a red trapezoid and identify the yellow hexagon as one whole when the blue rhombus is $\frac{1}{3}$.

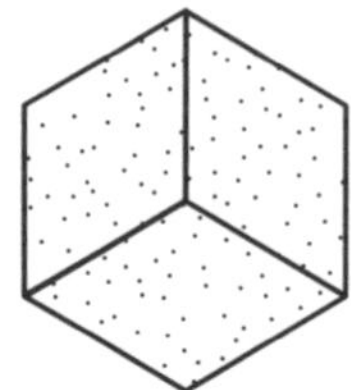

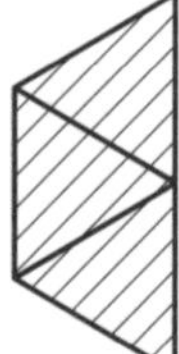

Figure 18: *Showing thirds using pattern blocks*

Question 18 asks students to name the fractions that different pattern blocks represent if the red trapezoid is one whole, and ***Question 19*** asks them to do the same when the yellow hexagon is one whole. Answering these questions will help students solve the puzzles posed in Lesson 8 *Fraction Puzzles.* Note that ***Question 18F*** asks for the fraction name for five green triangles if the red trapezoid is one whole. See Figure 19. Students can give either the improper fraction ($\frac{5}{3}$) or the mixed number $1\frac{2}{3}$. Point out to students that both answers are correct and represent the same quantity.

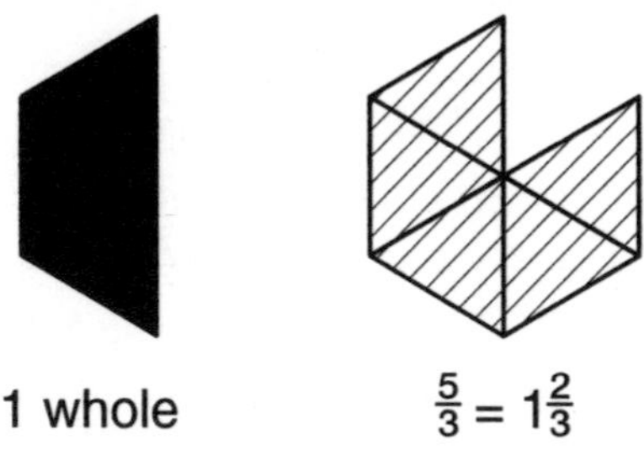

Figure 19: *If the red trapezoid is one whole, five green triangles are $\frac{5}{3}$ or $1\frac{2}{3}$.*

Part 4. Fraction Sentences

Questions 20–26 ask students to model easy addition problems using pattern blocks. Although they do not learn pencil-and-paper procedures for adding unlike fractions until fifth grade, using manipulatives provides students with a strategy for adding unlike fractions without finding common denominators. For example, ***Question 23*** asks them to show $\frac{1}{2}$ using two or more colors and then to write a number sentence for their results. Figure 20 shows a red trapezoid ($\frac{1}{2}$) covered by a green triangle ($\frac{1}{6}$) and a blue rhombus ($\frac{1}{3}$). Students write $\frac{1}{2} = \frac{1}{6} + \frac{1}{3}$ to represent this figure.

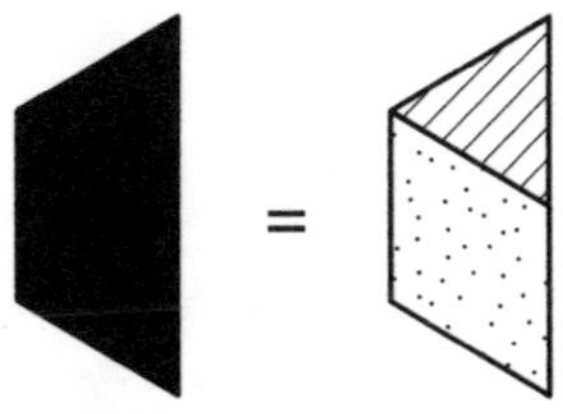

Figure 20: $\frac{1}{2} = \frac{1}{6} + \frac{1}{3}$

Journal Prompt

Ana walked half a block from her house to her aunt's house. Jacob walked half a block from his house to the store. Did Ana and Jacob walk the same distance? Explain your answer.

20. Show $\frac{1}{2}$ using green blocks. (Cover a red trapezoid with green blocks.) Write a number sentence to represent this figure.
21. The blue rhombus is $\frac{1}{3}$. Show $\frac{1}{3}$ using green blocks and write a number sentence to represent this figure.

We can show 1 whole with two or more colors and write a number sentence to represent the figure.

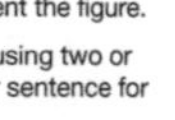

$1 = \frac{2}{4} + \frac{1}{6} + \frac{1}{3}$

22. Show 1 whole another way using two or more colors. Write a number sentence for your figure.

For Questions 23–26, show each fraction using two or more colors. Write a number sentence for each figure.

23. Show $\frac{1}{2}$.
24. Show $\frac{3}{4}$.
25. Show $\frac{2}{3}$.
26. Show $\frac{3}{2}$.

Homework

Use your fraction chart, the Fraction Chart in Lesson 3, or imagine pattern blocks to help you solve these problems.

1. Michael used $\frac{1}{2}$ yard of ribbon to decorate a gift for his mother. Irma used $\frac{2}{3}$ yard for her mother's present. Who used more ribbon?
2. Lee Yah drank $\frac{1}{3}$ cup of juice and Roberto drank $\frac{1}{2}$ cup. Who drank more juice?
3. Put these fractions in order from smallest to largest: $\frac{5}{6}, \frac{1}{4}, \frac{1}{2}$.
4. Put these fractions in order from smallest to largest: $\frac{1}{2}, \frac{1}{3}, \frac{3}{4}$.
5. Put these fractions in order from smallest to largest: $\frac{2}{3}, \frac{1}{2}, \frac{1}{6}$. Explain your strategy.
6. Add or subtract.
   A. $\frac{2}{6} + \frac{3}{6} =$
   B. $\frac{1}{4} + \frac{2}{4} =$
   C. $\frac{1}{3} + \frac{2}{3} =$
   D. $\frac{3}{4} - \frac{1}{4} =$
   E. $\frac{5}{6} - \frac{2}{6} =$
   F. $\frac{3}{3} - \frac{1}{3} =$
7. Write three equivalent fractions for $\frac{3}{4}$.

Pattern Block Fractions SG · Grade 4 · Unit 12 · Lesson 6 349

***Student Guide* - Page 349**

Daily Practice and Problems: Task and Challenge for Lesson 6

N. Challenge: Area (URG p. 18)

1. Draw two different shapes on *Centimeter Grid Paper.* Each shape should have an area of 21.5 square centimeters.
2. Measure the perimeter of your two shapes to the nearest tenth of a centimeter. Are the perimeters the same or different?

P. Task: Division Stories (URG p. 19)

Write a division story for 28 ÷ 9. Draw a picture for your story and write a number sentence that describes it. In your story, explain any remainder.

Name ______________________ Date ____________

Part 4 Fractions and Decimals

Complete this table. The flat equals one whole.

Base-Ten Shorthand	Common Fraction	Decimal Fraction
|| ·····	$\frac{25}{100}$ or $\frac{1}{4}$	0.25
□·		
		0.03
□□□□□ ||||||		
	$\frac{3}{10}$	
		4.37
□□····		
	$4\frac{16}{100}$	
		10.41

Part 5 A Fraction of a Meter

Use your fraction chart from Lesson 3, the Fraction Chart in your *Student Guide*, or a meterstick to help you compare fractions.

1. Name a measurement that is greater than $\frac{1}{2}$ meter but less than $\frac{7}{10}$ of a meter.
2. Which is longer: $\frac{7}{10}$ of a meter or 50 centimeters?
3. Name a measurement that is a little less than $\frac{3}{10}$ of a meter.
4. Name a fraction of a meter that is longer than $\frac{5}{100}$ of a meter and shorter than 0.2 meter.
5. Name a fraction that is less than $\frac{7}{10}$ but more than $\frac{1}{5}$.
6. Name a measurement that is longer than 1.54 meters but shorter than $1\frac{9}{10}$ meters.
7. Name a measurement that is more than three times as long as $\frac{1}{2}$ of a meter.

EXPLORING FRACTIONS DAB • Grade 4 • Unit 12 195

Discovery Assignment Book - Page 195

Suggestions for Teaching the Lesson

Math Facts

DPP Bit M provides practice with the division facts for the nines through the use of fact families. Task P asks students to write a story for a division problem.

Homework and Practice

- The Homework section in the *Student Guide* reviews skills and concepts developed in the first five lessons of this unit.
- DPP Bit O poses a divisibility question and asks students to explain their strategies.
- Remind students to practice the division facts for the nines using their *Triangle Flash Cards.*
- Assign Home Practice Parts 4 and 5. Students will need their fraction charts and a meterstick for Part 5.

Answers for Parts 4 and 5 of the Home Practice can be found in the Answer Key at the end of this lesson and at the end of this unit.

Assessment

- Use the *Observational Assessment Record* to note students' abilities to identify the whole when given a fractional part of the whole.
- Check students' homework to assess their abilities to compare fractions, add and subtract fractions with like denominators, and find equivalent fractions.

Extension

DPP Challenge N provides an open-response problem concerning area and perimeter.

AT A GLANCE

Math Facts and Daily Practice and Problems

DPP Bit M provides practice with math facts. Items O and P focus on different aspects of division. Challenge N provides a problem involving area and perimeter.

Before the Activity

If students are new to the curriculum or if they have not had experience using pattern blocks to represent fractions, students can complete a third-grade activity found in the Unit Resource Guide, *What's 1?,* to introduce pattern block fractions.

Part 1. When Are Halves Different?

1. Students read the first section on the *Pattern Block Fractions* Activity Pages in the *Student Guide.*
2. Discuss ***Questions 1–2.***

Part 2. Exploring Pattern Blocks

1. Distribute one set of pattern blocks to each pair of students.
2. Students explore pattern block fractions by completing ***Questions 3–13*** in the *Student Guide.*

Part 3. Exploring Pattern Block Fractions

Students identify wholes from given fractions using pattern blocks in ***Questions 14–19.***

Part 4. Fraction Sentences

Students model easy addition and subtraction problems using pattern blocks in ***Questions 20–26.***

Homework

1. Assign ***Questions 1–7*** in the Homework section of the *Student Guide.* These questions review skills and concepts addressed in Lessons 1–5.
2. Assign Home Practice Parts 4 and 5.
3. Students continue practicing division facts using the *Triangle Flash Cards: 9s.*

Assessment

Use the *Observational Assessment Record* to note students' abilities to identify the whole when given a fractional part of the whole.

Notes:

Name ______________________________ Date ______________

What's 1?

Use yellow hexagons, red trapezoids, blue rhombuses, and green triangles to answer the following questions.

Covering Pattern Blocks

1. Look at all your pieces to answer these questions.
   - **A.** How many red trapezoids cover one yellow hexagon?
   - **B.** How many blue rhombuses cover one yellow hexagon?
   - **C.** How many green triangles cover one yellow hexagon?
   - **D.** How many green triangles cover one blue rhombus?
   - **E.** How many green triangles cover one red trapezoid?
   - **F.** Use two different colors to cover one red trapezoid. What did you use?

Wholes to Parts

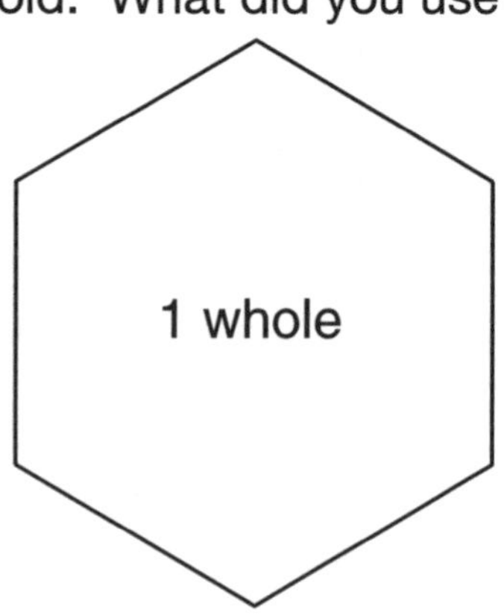

2. If the yellow hexagon is one whole, then:
   - **A.** What piece is one-half?
   - **B.** What piece is one-third?
   - **C.** What piece is one-sixth?
   - **D.** We can write $\frac{2}{6}$ for 2 green triangles. Write a number for 5 green triangles.
   - **E.** Write a number for 2 blue rhombuses.
   - **F.** Write a number for 3 red trapezoids.
   - **G.** Write a number for 4 red trapezoids.
   - **H.** Is 1 blue rhombus more or less than one-half?
   - **I.** Are 2 blue rhombuses more or less than one-half?

3. This shape is one whole.

   1 whole

   - **A.** How many blue rhombuses cover the shape?
   - **B.** How many green triangles cover the shape?
   - **C.** What piece is one-half?
   - **D.** What piece is one-fourth?
   - **E.** Write a fraction for 3 green triangles.
   - **F.** What other piece makes the same fraction as 3 green triangles?
   - **G.** Is 1 red trapezoid more or less than one-half?

Name ______________________________ Date ______________

Parts to Wholes

4. If the green triangle is one-half, what piece is one whole?

5. If the blue rhombus is one-third, what is one whole?

6. Trace pattern blocks on a sheet of paper to answer these questions. For example, if the green triangle is $\frac{1}{3}$, draw one whole.

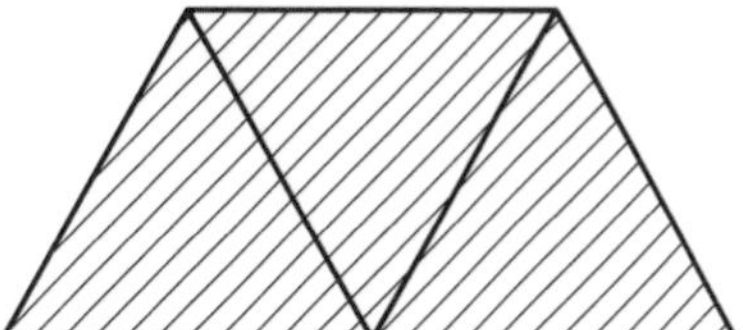

   A. If the green triangle is $\frac{1}{3}$, draw $\frac{2}{3}$.
   B. If the green triangle is $\frac{1}{5}$, draw one whole.
   C. If the red trapezoid is $\frac{1}{3}$, draw one whole.
   D. If the yellow hexagon is $\frac{1}{2}$, draw one whole.
   E. If the blue rhombus is $\frac{1}{4}$, draw $\frac{3}{4}$.

7. The shape to the right is one whole.
   A. How many green triangles cover the shape?
   B. Write a common fraction for 1 green triangle.
   C. Write a decimal for 1 green triangle.
   D. Write a fraction and a decimal for 7 green triangles.
   E. Write a fraction and a decimal for 5 green triangles.

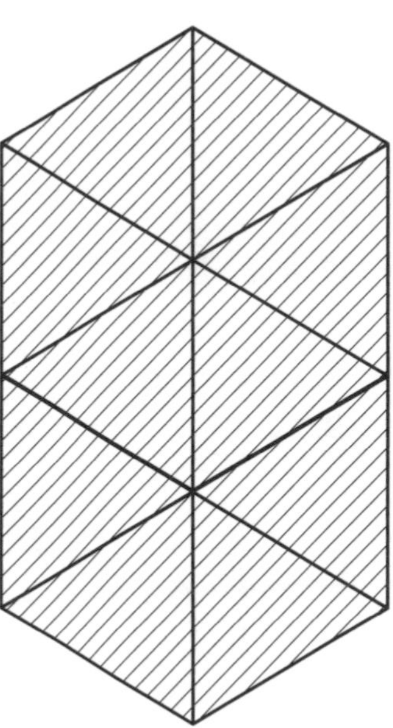

8. The shape to the right is one whole.
   A. How many blue rhombuses cover the whole?
   B. Write a common fraction for 1 blue rhombus.
   C. Write a different fraction for 1 blue rhombus.
   D. Write a decimal for 1 blue rhombus.
   E. Write a fraction for 1 yellow hexagon.
   F. Is 1 yellow hexagon more or less than one-half?

9. A. If the blue rhombus is one whole, write a number for 3 green triangles.
   B. If the blue rhombus is one whole, write a number for 1 yellow hexagon.

Student Guide

Questions 1–26 (SG pp. 346–349)

1. *No, because the drop heights for each one are different.
2. *When the wholes are different in size.
3. *4
4. 2
5. 2
6. less than
7. 6
8. greater than
9. 6
10. 3
11. 3
12. 4
13. greater than
14. A. *green triangle
    B. *yellow hexagon
    C.
15. A.   
    B. red trapezoid
    C. blue rhombus
    D. red trapezoid
16. A. brown trapezoid
    B. 
    C. 
17. A. yellow hexagon
    B.
    C. 
18. A. *$\frac{1}{3}$
    B. $\frac{2}{3}$
    C. $\frac{2}{3}$
    D. $\frac{1}{2}$
    E. $1\frac{1}{2}$ or $\frac{3}{2}$
    F. *$1\frac{2}{3}$ or $\frac{5}{3}$
19. A. *$\frac{1}{2}$
    B. $\frac{1}{4}$
    C. $\frac{2}{4}$
    D. $\frac{1}{3}$
    E. $\frac{2}{6}$
    F. $\frac{2}{3}$
    G. $\frac{3}{2}$ or $1\frac{1}{2}$
20. $\frac{3}{6} = \frac{1}{2}$ or $\frac{1}{6} + \frac{1}{6} + \frac{1}{6} = \frac{1}{2}$

21. $\frac{1}{3} = \frac{2}{6}$ or $\frac{1}{6} + \frac{1}{6} = \frac{1}{3}$

22. Answers will vary.

*Answers and/or discussion are included in the Lesson Guide.

**Answers for all the Home Practice in the *Discovery Assignment Book* are at the end of the unit.

23. $*\frac{1}{3} + \frac{1}{6} = \frac{1}{2}$

24. Answers will vary. Two possible answers:

$\frac{1}{2} + \frac{1}{4} = \frac{3}{4}$

$\frac{3}{6} + \frac{1}{4} = \frac{3}{4}$

25. $\frac{2}{6} + \frac{1}{3} = \frac{2}{3}$

26. Answers will vary. Two possible answers:

$\frac{1}{2} + \frac{1}{6} + \frac{1}{3} + \frac{2}{4} = \frac{3}{2}$

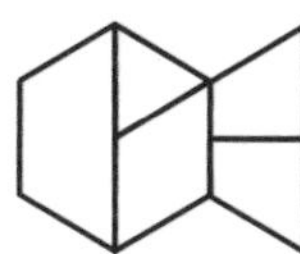

$\frac{1}{2} + \frac{4}{4} = \frac{3}{2}$

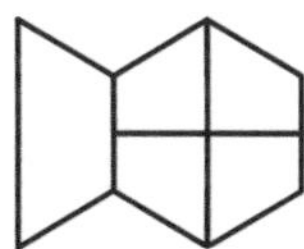

Homework (SG p. 349)

Questions 1–7

1. Irma
2. Roberto
3. $\frac{1}{4}, \frac{1}{2}, \frac{5}{6}$
4. $\frac{1}{3}, \frac{1}{2}, \frac{3}{4}$
5. $\frac{1}{6}, \frac{1}{2}, \frac{2}{3}$; Possible strategies include using the fraction chart or using $\frac{1}{2}$ as a benchmark. $\frac{1}{6}$ is less than $\frac{1}{2}$ and $\frac{2}{3}$ is more than $\frac{1}{2}$.
6. A. $\frac{5}{6}$
   B. $\frac{3}{4}$
   C. $\frac{3}{3}$ or 1
   D. $\frac{2}{4}$
   E. $\frac{3}{6}$
   F. $\frac{2}{3}$
7. Answers will vary.

Discovery Assignment Book

**** Home Practice (DAB p. 195)**

Part 4. Fractions and Decimals

Base-Ten Shorthand	Common Fraction	Decimal Fraction
\/ ·····	$\frac{25}{100}$ or $\frac{1}{4}$	0.25
□·	$1\frac{1}{100}$	1.01
···	$\frac{3}{100}$	0.03
□□□□□ /\/\\	$5\frac{5}{10}$ or $5\frac{1}{2}$	5.5
/\/	$\frac{3}{10}$	0.3
□□□□ //\ ::···	$4\frac{37}{100}$	4.37
□□····	$2\frac{4}{100}$	2.04
□□□□ /:····	$4\frac{16}{100}$	4.16
■\/\\.	$10\frac{41}{100}$	10.41

Part 5. A Fraction of a Meter

Questions 1–7

1. Answers will vary. Possible response: $\frac{6}{10}$ m
2. $\frac{7}{10}$ of a meter
3. Answers will vary. Possible responses: 25 cm or 0.25 m
4. Answers will vary. Possible response: $\frac{1}{10}$ m
5. Answers will vary. Possible response: $\frac{1}{2}$
6. Answers will vary. Possible responses: $1\frac{3}{4}$ or 1.75 meters
7. Answers will vary. Possible response: 2 meters

*Answers and/or discussion are included in the Lesson Guide.

**Answers for all the Home Practice in the *Discovery Assignment Book* are at the end of the unit.

Unit Resource Guide

What's 1? (URG pp. 72–73)

Questions 1–9

1. A. 2
   B. 3
   C. 6
   D. 2
   E. 3
   F. 1 blue rhombus and 1 green triangle
2. A. red trapezoid
   B. blue rhombus
   C. green triangle
   D. $\frac{5}{6}$
   E. $\frac{2}{3}$
   F. $1\frac{1}{2}$ or $\frac{3}{2}$
   G. $\frac{4}{2}$ or 2
   H. less
   I. more
3. A. 2
   B. 4
   C. blue rhombus
   D. green triangle
   E. $\frac{3}{4}$
   F. red trapezoid
   G. more
4. blue rhombus
5. yellow hexagon
6. A. 
   B. * 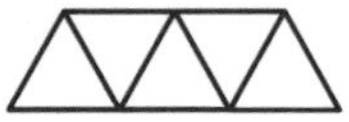
   C. 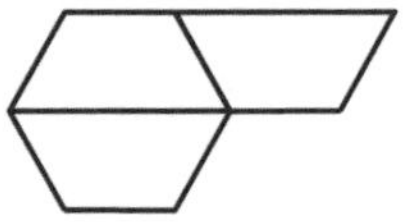
   D. 
   E. 
7. A. *10
   B. *$\frac{1}{10}$
   C. *0.1
   D. $\frac{7}{10}$ and 0.7
   E. *$\frac{5}{10}$ or $\frac{1}{2}$ and 0.5
8. A. 5
   B. *$\frac{2}{10}$ or $\frac{1}{5}$
   C. *$\frac{1}{5}$ or $\frac{2}{10}$
   D. *0.2
   E. $\frac{6}{10}$ or $\frac{3}{5}$
   F. more
9. A. $\frac{3}{2}$ or $1\frac{1}{2}$
   B. 3

*Answers and/or discussion are included in the Lesson Guide.
**Answers for all the Home Practice in the *Discovery Assignment Book* are at the end of the unit.

LESSON GUIDE 

Solving Problems with Pattern Blocks

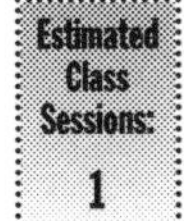

Students use pattern blocks to solve word problems involving the ordering of fractions. Using the context of dividing food fairly, they investigate the relationship between the number of equal parts in the whole (the size of the denominator) and the size of the fraction. For example, they can reason that $\frac{1}{3}$ is greater than $\frac{1}{4}$ because if you divide a pizza into four parts, the parts will be smaller than if you divide the pizza into three parts. Students also use pattern blocks to solve word problems involving addition of fractions.

Key Content

- Solving multistep word problems.
- Comparing and ordering fractions.
- Adding fractions using manipulatives.
- Connecting mathematics to real-world situations.

Daily Practice and Problems: Bit for Lesson 7

Q. Confused! (URG p. 19) 

On planet Zimbo, a Zimbonese was told that the number 6 was larger than the number 4. But now there is confusion because the Zimbonese has also been told that $\frac{1}{6}$ is smaller than $\frac{1}{4}$. Please use a diagram to explain why $\frac{1}{6}$ is smaller than $\frac{1}{4}$.

The DPP Task is on page 80. Suggestions for using the DPPs are on page 80.

Materials List

Print Materials for Students

		Math Facts and Daily Practice and Problems	Lab	Homework	Written Assessment
Student Books	Student Guide		*Solving Problems with Pattern Blocks* Pages 350–351 and Fraction Chart from *Comparing Fractions* Page 336	*Solving Problems with Pattern Blocks* Homework Section Page 352	
Teacher Resources	Unit Resource Guide	DPP Items Q–R Pages 19–20 (CD)			DPP Item Q *Confused!* Page 19 and DPP Item R *Further Confusion* Page 20 (CD)

(CD) *available on Teacher Resource CD*

All Transparency Masters, Blackline Masters, and Assessment Blackline Masters in the Unit Resource Guide are on the Teacher Resource CD.

Supplies for Each Student Pair

set of pattern blocks (at least 2 to 3 yellow hexagons, 6 red trapezoids, 10 blue rhombuses, 10 green triangles, 6 brown trapezoids)
fraction chart made in Lesson 3

Materials for the Teacher

overhead pattern blocks, optional

Developing the Activity

Students can work in pairs to complete ***Questions 1–8*** on the *Solving Problems with Pattern Blocks* Activity Pages in the *Student Guide.* Then, the student pairs can report their strategies and solutions to the class.

Questions 1–3 ask students to name fractions when the whole is divided into different numbers of equal parts and then to compare the fractions. For example, to answer ***Question 2***, students find that John ate $\frac{2}{12}$ of a pie, Shannon ate $\frac{2}{6}$ of a pie, and Brandon ate $\frac{2}{4}$ of a pie. They must then decide who ate the most and the least amount of pie. Students can reason that when the pies are divided into more pieces, the pieces will be smaller. ***Question 3*** is a whimsical version of the same problem using nonsense words. Students may use their fraction chart from Lesson 3 to help them think through the problem. If one whole is divided into eight zax and the same size whole is divided into ten snarks, what fraction is one zax? What fraction is one snark? Which fraction is larger? One zax is $\frac{1}{8}$ of the whole and one snark is $\frac{1}{10}$. One-eighth is larger since the whole has been divided into fewer pieces.

Question 4 asks students to order fractions which have like numerators and unlike denominators. They solved similar problems using the Fraction Chart in Lesson 3. ***Questions 4A–4B*** can also be modeled using pattern blocks. ***Questions 4C–4D*** can be solved using the Fraction Chart or using the reasoning they developed answering ***Questions 1–3***.

Question 5 asks students to describe a strategy for ordering fractions if the numerators are the same. One possible response: "When the numerators are the same, the smaller the denominator, the larger the fraction because the whole is divided into fewer parts."

Questions 6–8 are word problems which involve adding fractions. Some of the problems in ***Question 6*** involve adding fractions with unlike denominators, so they will need to use tools such as pattern blocks (as they did in Lesson 6) or drawings to solve the problems. By solving problems using manipulatives, students build a conceptual foundation for pencil and paper procedures and they develop number sense with fractions. ***Questions 7–8*** are problems that can be solved using repeated addition. Students may choose to write an addition number sentence or a

Solving Problems with Pattern Blocks

You may use pattern blocks or your fraction chart to help you solve these problems.

1. Wednesday is pizza day at Bessie Coleman School. Each table in the lunchroom gets one pizza to share fairly among the students at the table. There are three students at Table A and four students at Table B.
   A. What fraction of the pizza will each student at Table A eat?
   B. What fraction of the pizza will each student at Table B eat?
   C. Who gets to eat more pizza, the students at Table A or the students at Table B?
   D. Which fraction is larger, $\frac{1}{3}$ or $\frac{1}{4}$? Explain how you know.
2. The cook made three small fruit pies that are all the same size. She divided the apple pie into 12 pieces, the cherry pie into six pieces, and the peach pie into four pieces. John ate two pieces of apple pie, Shannon ate two pieces of cherry pie, and Brandon ate two pieces of peach pie.

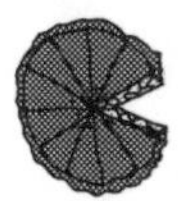

   A. What fraction of the apple pie did John eat?
   B. What fraction of the cherry pie did Shannon eat?
   C. What fraction of the peach pie did Brandon eat?
   D. Who ate the most pie? Tell how you know.
   E. Who ate the least pie?
3. One whole is divided into eight zax. Each zax is the same size. The same size whole is divided into ten snarks. Each snark is the same size.
   A. What fraction of the whole is one zax?
   B. What fraction of the whole is one snark?
   C. Which is larger, one zax or one snark? Explain.

350 SG • Grade 4 • Unit 12 • Lesson 7 Solving Problems with Pattern Blocks

***Student Guide* - Page 350**

4. Put each group of fractions in order from smallest to largest.
   A. $\frac{1}{2}, \frac{1}{6}, \frac{1}{3}, \frac{1}{4}, \frac{1}{12}$
   B. $\frac{2}{6}, \frac{2}{3}, \frac{2}{4}, \frac{2}{12}$
   C. $\frac{1}{10}, \frac{1}{8}, \frac{1}{5}$
   D. $\frac{3}{10}, \frac{3}{8}, \frac{3}{5}$
5. Describe a strategy for ordering fractions if the numerators are the same.

To solve the problems in Questions 6–8, you may use any tools such as pattern blocks, the Fraction Chart in Lesson 3, or pictures. Write number sentences to record your solutions.

6. Each of the following pairs of students shared a pizza. How much of the whole pizza did each pair eat?
   A. Manny ate $\frac{1}{2}$ of a pizza and Ming ate $\frac{1}{4}$ of it.
   B. Michael ate $\frac{3}{8}$ of a pizza and Frank ate $\frac{5}{8}$ of the pizza.
   C. Felicia ate $\frac{1}{3}$ of a pizza. Linda ate $\frac{1}{6}$ of it.
   D. Lee Yah ate $\frac{5}{12}$ and David ate $\frac{2}{12}$.
7. A. Four students each ate $\frac{1}{2}$ of a muffin. How many muffins did they eat altogether?
   B. Five students each ate $\frac{1}{2}$ of a muffin. How many muffins did they eat altogether?

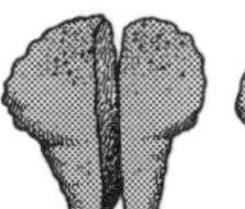
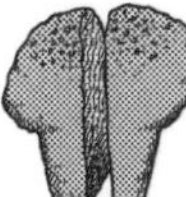
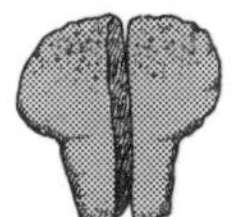

8. A. Eight students each ate $\frac{1}{4}$ of an apple. How many apples did they eat altogether?
   B. Three students each ate $\frac{1}{4}$ of an apple. How many apples did they eat altogether?
   C. Six students each ate $\frac{1}{4}$ of an apple. How many apples did they eat altogether?

Solving Problems with Pattern Blocks SG • Grade 4 • Unit 12 • Lesson 7 351

***Student Guide* - Page 351**

Journal Prompt

One whole is divided equally into 100 widgets. The same size whole is divided into 50 zittles. What fraction of a whole is one widget? What fraction of a whole is one zittle? Which is larger, a widget or a zittle? Explain.

Daily Practice and Problems: Task for Lesson 7

R. Task: Further Confusion (URG p. 20) N

Brandon and Lee Yah invited the Zimbonese to eat pizza with them. Brandon has $\frac{1}{8}$ of a pizza and it is bigger in size than Lee Yah's $\frac{1}{4}$ of a pizza. The Zimbonese thought it understood (see DPP Bit Q) that $\frac{1}{8}$ was smaller than $\frac{1}{4}$. What needs to be changed so that $\frac{1}{8}$ is less than $\frac{1}{4}$?

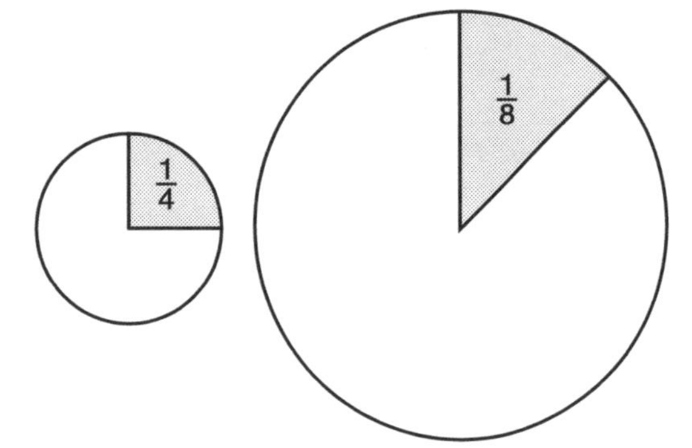

multiplication number sentence. For example, *Question 7A* asks how many muffins are eaten if four students each eat $\frac{1}{2}$ of a muffin. After modeling the problem with pattern blocks, students may write $\frac{1}{2} + \frac{1}{2} + \frac{1}{2} + \frac{1}{2} = 2$ muffins or $4 \times \frac{1}{2} = 2$ muffins.

Suggestions for Teaching the Lesson

Homework and Practice

Questions 1–5 in the Homework section of the *Student Guide* provide practice ordering fractions, finding equivalent fractions, and adding fractions with like denominators.

Assessment

Use DPP items Q and R to assess students' understanding of fraction concepts.

Homework

1. Write these fractions in order from smallest to largest.
   - A. $\frac{3}{12}, \frac{3}{4}, \frac{3}{3}, \frac{3}{6}$
   - B. $\frac{3}{5}, \frac{3}{10}, \frac{3}{8}, \frac{3}{4}$
   - C. $\frac{3}{8}, \frac{1}{8}, \frac{5}{8}, \frac{8}{8}$
   - D. $\frac{1}{2}, \frac{1}{12}, \frac{5}{6}$
2. On Sunday, Shannon's family ate $\frac{5}{12}$ of a casserole. On Monday they ate $\frac{3}{12}$ of the casserole. How much of the casserole did they eat? How much is left over?

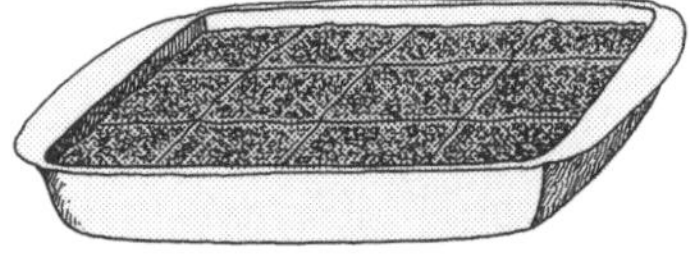

3. On Friday, a worker painted $\frac{3}{8}$ of a fence. On Saturday, he painted another $\frac{3}{8}$ of the fence.
   - A. How much of the fence did he paint on the two days?
   - B. How much more of the fence does he have left to paint?
4. Complete the following number sentences.
   - A. $\frac{3}{4} = \frac{?}{20}$
   - B. $\frac{3}{6} = \frac{5}{?}$
   - C. $\frac{2}{3} = \frac{6}{?}$
   - D. $\frac{3}{8} = \frac{?}{16}$
   - E. $\frac{1}{2} = \frac{?}{6}$
   - F. $\frac{30}{100} = \frac{3}{?}$
5. A. Four children each ate $\frac{1}{3}$ of a large cookie. How many cookies did they eat altogether?
   - B. Six children each ate $\frac{1}{3}$ of a large cookie. How many cookies did they eat altogether?

352 SG · Grade 4 · Unit 12 · Lesson 7 — Solving Problems with Pattern Blocks

Student Guide - Page 352

AT A GLANCE

Math Facts and Daily Practice and Problems

DPP items Q and R review basic fraction concepts.

Developing the Activity

1. Students solve problems on the *Solving Problems with Pattern Blocks* Activity Pages in the *Student Guide.* They order fractions and develop strategies for comparing fractions with like numerators ***(Questions 1–5)***.
2. Students solve problems involving addition of fractions using manipulatives or drawings ***(Questions 6–8)***.

Homework

Assign ***Questions 1–5*** in the Homework section in the *Student Guide.*

Assessment

Use DPP items Q and R as assessments.

Notes:

Student Guide

Questions 1–8 (SG pp. 350–351)

1. A. $\frac{1}{3}$ pizza
   B. $\frac{1}{4}$ pizza
   C. Table A
   D. $\frac{1}{3}$; There are three students at Table A and 4 students at Table B. Since the pizza at Table A was divided into fewer pieces, each piece is bigger than the 4 pieces at Table B.
2. A. *$\frac{2}{12}$ pie
   B. *$\frac{2}{6}$ pie
   C. *$\frac{2}{4}$ pie
   D. Brandon ate the most pie because his pie was divided into fewer pieces, so each piece is larger.
   E. John
3. A. *$\frac{1}{8}$
   B. *$\frac{1}{10}$
   C. *One zax is larger than a snark since the whole is divided into fewer pieces to make a zax than to make a snark.
4. A. *$\frac{1}{12}, \frac{1}{6}, \frac{1}{4}, \frac{1}{3}, \frac{1}{2}$
   B. *$\frac{2}{12}, \frac{2}{6}, \frac{2}{4}, \frac{2}{3}$
   C. *$\frac{1}{10}, \frac{1}{8}, \frac{1}{5}$
   D. *$\frac{3}{10}, \frac{3}{8}, \frac{3}{5}$
5. *When the numerators are the same, the fraction with the smaller denominator is the larger fraction.
6. A. *$\frac{1}{2} + \frac{1}{4} = \frac{3}{4}$ pizza
   B. *$\frac{3}{8} + \frac{5}{8} = \frac{8}{8}$ or 1 whole pizza
   C. *$\frac{1}{3} + \frac{1}{6} = \frac{1}{2}$ pizza
   D. *$\frac{5}{12} + \frac{2}{12} = \frac{7}{12}$ pizza
7. A. *$\frac{1}{2} + \frac{1}{2} + \frac{1}{2} + \frac{1}{2} = 2$ muffins or $4 \times \frac{1}{2} = 2$ muffins
   B. $\frac{1}{2} + \frac{1}{2} + \frac{1}{2} + \frac{1}{2} + \frac{1}{2} = \frac{5}{2}$ or $2\frac{1}{2}$ muffins or $5 \times \frac{1}{2} = \frac{5}{2}$ or $2\frac{1}{2}$ muffins
8. A. $\frac{1}{4} + \frac{1}{4} + \frac{1}{4} + \frac{1}{4} + \frac{1}{4} + \frac{1}{4} + \frac{1}{4} + \frac{1}{4} = 2$ apples or $8 \times \frac{1}{4} = 2$ apples
   B. $\frac{1}{4} + \frac{1}{4} + \frac{1}{4} = \frac{3}{4}$ apple or $3 \times \frac{1}{4} = \frac{3}{4}$ apple
   C. $\frac{1}{4} + \frac{1}{4} + \frac{1}{4} + \frac{1}{4} + \frac{1}{4} + \frac{1}{4} = \frac{6}{4}$ or $1\frac{1}{2}$ apples or $6 \times \frac{1}{4} = 1\frac{1}{2}$ apples

Homework (SG p. 352)

Questions 1–5

1. A. $\frac{3}{12}, \frac{3}{6}, \frac{3}{4}, \frac{3}{3}$
   B. $\frac{3}{10}, \frac{3}{8}, \frac{3}{5}, \frac{3}{4}$
   C. $\frac{1}{8}, \frac{3}{8}, \frac{5}{8}, \frac{8}{8}$
   D. $\frac{1}{12}, \frac{1}{2}, \frac{5}{6}$
2. They ate $\frac{8}{12}$ of the casserole. There is $\frac{4}{12}$ of the casserole left over.
3. A. $\frac{6}{8}$ of the fence
   B. $\frac{2}{8}$ of the fence
4. A. $\frac{3}{4} = \frac{15}{20}$
   B. $\frac{3}{6} = \frac{5}{10}$
   C. $\frac{2}{3} = \frac{6}{9}$
   D. $\frac{3}{8} = \frac{6}{16}$
   E. $\frac{1}{2} = \frac{3}{6}$
   F. $\frac{30}{100} = \frac{3}{10}$
5. A. $\frac{1}{3} + \frac{1}{3} + \frac{1}{3} + \frac{1}{3} = \frac{4}{3}$ or $1\frac{1}{3}$ cookie or $4 \times \frac{1}{3} = \frac{4}{3}$ or $1\frac{1}{3}$ cookie
   B. $\frac{1}{3} + \frac{1}{3} + \frac{1}{3} + \frac{1}{3} + \frac{1}{3} + \frac{1}{3} = 2$ cookies or $6 \times \frac{1}{3} = 2$ cookies

*Answers and/or discussion are included in the Lesson Guide.

**Answers for all the Home Practice in the *Discovery Assignment Book* are at the end of the unit.

LESSON GUIDE 

Fraction Puzzles

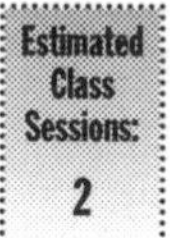

Given clues, students work in cooperative groups of four to solve fraction puzzles. After solving the fourth fraction puzzle, students will work independently to explain their solution and to communicate their problem-solving strategies. The Student Rubrics: *Solving* and *Telling* are used as guides for exemplary work.

Key Content

- Representing fractions using pattern blocks and diagrams.
- Working cooperatively to solve problems.
- Solving open-response problems and communicating problem-solving strategies.
- Writing number sentences using fractions.

Daily Practice and Problems: Bits for Lesson 8

S. Words to Numbers (URG p. 20) 

1. Write the following words as numbers.

   A. two-thirds B. six-tenths

   C. five-eighths D. one-twelfth

2. Write the following numbers as words.

   A. $\frac{3}{4}$ B. $\frac{7}{9}$

   C. $\frac{1}{2}$ D. $\frac{2}{5}$

U. Even Products (URG p. 21) N

In your journal, explain why all the multiples of 4 are even numbers. First, write all the multiples in order from 4 to 40.

The DPP Challenges are on page 87. Suggestions for using the DPPs are on page 87.

Materials List

Print Materials for Students

		Math Facts and Daily Practice and Problems	Assessment Activity	Homework	Written Assessment
Student Books	Student Guide		*Fraction Puzzles* Pages 353–354 and Student Rubrics: *Solving* Appendix B, *Telling* Appendix C, and Inside Back Cover (CD)	*Fraction Puzzles* Homework Section Pages 354–355 and Fraction Chart from *Comparing Fractions* Page 336	
Student Books	Discovery Assignment Book			Home Practice Part 6 Page 196	
Teacher Resource	Unit Resource Guide	DPP Items S–V Pages 20–22 (CD)	*Fraction Puzzle Clues* Pages 90–91, 1 per group		*Puzzle Problem* Page 92, 1 per student

(CD) *available on Teacher Resource CD*

All Transparency Masters, Blackline Masters, and Assessment Blackline Masters in the Unit Resource Guide are on the Teacher Resource CD.

Supplies for Each Student Group of Four

set of pattern blocks

Materials for the Teacher

poster or transparency of the Student Rubric: *Solving* (Teacher Implementation Guide, Assessment section)
poster or transparency of the Student Rubric: *Telling* (Teacher Implementation Guide, Assessment section)
TIMS Multidimensional Rubric (Teacher Implementation Guide, Assessment section)
Observational Assessment Record (Unit Resource Guide, Pages 9–10 and Teacher Resource CD)
Individual Assessment Record Sheet (Teacher Implementation Guide, Assessment section and Teacher Resource CD)
envelopes, optional
paper clips, optional

Before the Activity

There are four different fraction puzzles and each group should solve all four. The clues for each puzzle are labeled with the same letter of the alphabet and are found on the *Fraction Puzzle Clues* Blackline Masters. Enough copies should be made so that each group has a set of clues for each puzzle. Puzzle D is an assessment and should be done after the other puzzles are completed.

Cut out the clue cards for each puzzle and paper-clip each set of cards together or place the clues for each puzzle in an envelope labeled with the puzzle letter. This will make it easier to hand out and collect the clues.

Copy each set of clues on colored paper using a different color for each puzzle letter. After cutting the clues out, they can be laminated so they can be used over again.

Developing the Activity

This activity has two parts: Puzzles A, B, and C and the assessment Puzzle D. Students work cooperatively in groups of four for both parts. Then, each student independently writes a full explanation of his or her group's solution and strategies for Puzzle D on a copy of the *Puzzle Problem* Assessment Blackline Master.

Part 1. Fraction Puzzles

Students will work in groups of four to solve puzzles using pattern blocks. Each group will work together to find a solution that they all agree upon.

Have students read the vignette on the *Fraction Puzzles* Activity Pages in the *Student Guide*. It introduces the rules for solving the fraction puzzles. Ask students to read the four clues that Roberto's group was given and to look at the solutions. ***Question 1*** asks students to look back at the clues to see if the group's solution satisfies all the guidelines they were given. Students should see that this is an acceptable solution. ***Question 2*** shows another group's solution to the same puzzle. Since this solution uses only green triangles, it does not meet the guidelines and is not acceptable.

TIMS Tip

Ask students what types of behavior will help their group be successful. Suggested behaviors include:

- Take turns speaking.
- Listen when someone else is talking.
- Respect everyone's ideas.
- Work together.
- Check the group's work for accuracy.
- Talk to the teacher only after the group has been consulted.

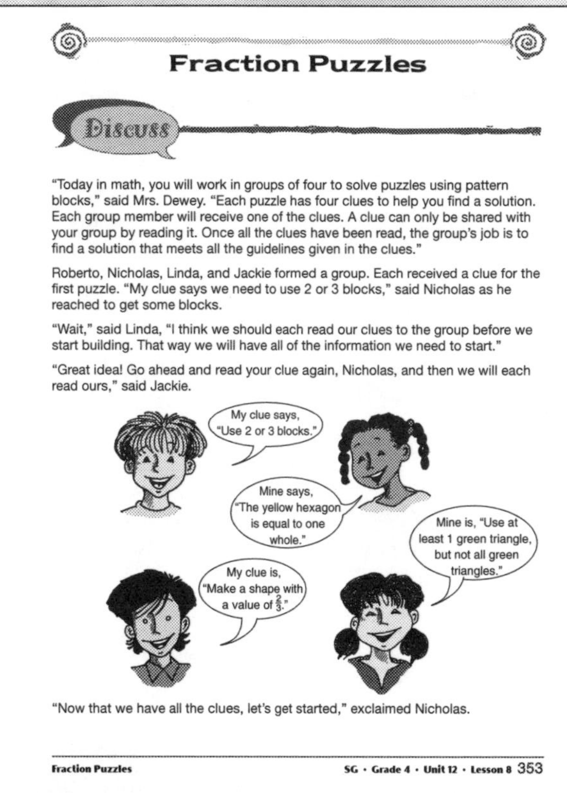

Fraction Puzzles

Discuss

"Today in math, you will work in groups of four to solve puzzles using pattern blocks," said Mrs. Dewey. "Each puzzle has four clues to help you find a solution. Each group member will receive one of the clues. A clue can only be shared with your group by reading it. Once all the clues have been read, the group's job is to find a solution that meets all the guidelines given in the clues."

Roberto, Nicholas, Linda, and Jackie formed a group. Each received a clue for the first puzzle. "My clue says we need to use 2 or 3 blocks," said Nicholas as he reached to get some blocks.

"Wait," said Linda, "I think we should each read our clues to the group before we start building. That way we will have all of the information we need to start."

"Great idea! Go ahead and read your clue again, Nicholas, and then we will each read ours," said Jackie.

"Now that we have all the clues, let's get started," exclaimed Nicholas.

Fraction Puzzles SG • Grade 4 • Unit 12 • Lesson 8 353

***Student Guide* - Page 353**

TIMS Tip

This activity works best in groups of four. However, if you have a group of three, give one student two clues to read. If you have a group of five, one student can act as the judge for the group, checking the final solution to make sure it meets all of the guidelines as specified in the clues. On the next puzzle, the role of judge will switch to a different student in the group.

After some work, the students found this solution: 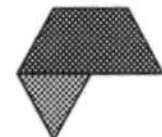

They wrote this number sentence to represent their solution: $\frac{1}{2} + \frac{1}{6} = \frac{2}{3}$.

1. Look back at their clues and see if this solution fits all the clues they were given.
2. One of the other groups found this solution to the same puzzle.

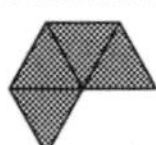

They wrote this number sentence: $\frac{1}{6} + \frac{1}{6} + \frac{1}{6} + \frac{1}{6} = \frac{2}{3}$. Look back at the clues. Does this solution fit all the clues that were given? Why or why not?

3. Find another solution to this puzzle. Use the clues provided to make sure your solution fits all of the clues. Draw a picture of your solution and write a number sentence to represent your solution.

Solve the following problems. You may use your fraction chart to help you.

1. Put the following fractions in order from smallest to largest.
   A. $\frac{1}{5}, \frac{1}{9}, \frac{1}{8}, \frac{1}{3}$ B. $\frac{3}{10}, \frac{3}{4}, \frac{3}{8}, \frac{3}{5}$ C. $\frac{2}{3}, \frac{3}{4}, \frac{5}{8}, \frac{1}{2}$ D. $\frac{2}{5}, \frac{3}{8}, \frac{5}{12}, \frac{1}{4}$
2. Put the following fractions in order from smallest to largest.
   A. $\frac{1}{3}, \frac{1}{5}, \frac{1}{2}, \frac{1}{8}$ B. $\frac{2}{6}, \frac{2}{4}, \frac{2}{5}, \frac{2}{10}$ C. $\frac{4}{5}, \frac{4}{12}, \frac{4}{8}, \frac{4}{6}$ D. $\frac{3}{8}, \frac{3}{10}, \frac{3}{5}, \frac{3}{4}$
   E. Explain a strategy for putting fractions in order when the numerators are all the same.

354 SG · Grade 4 · Unit 12 · Lesson 8 Fraction Puzzles

***Student Guide* - Page 354**

TIMS Tip

One strategy for sharing solutions is to pair two groups together. As each of the groups finish, they share their solutions with their partner group before showing it to you or recording it on paper.

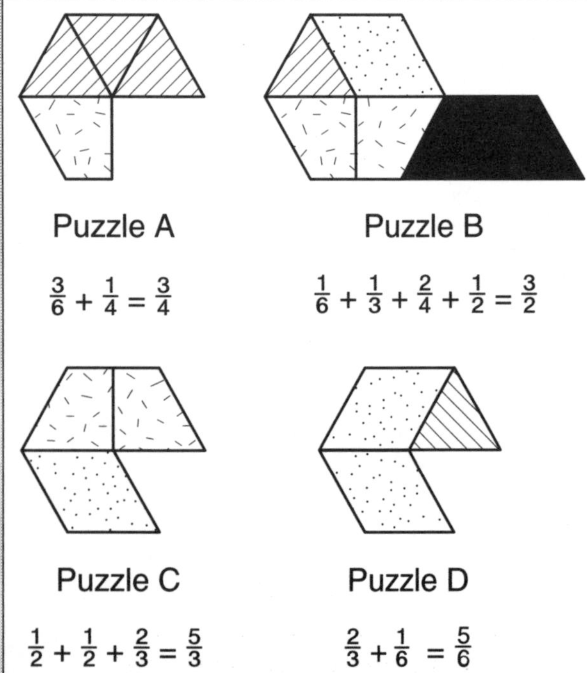

Figure 22: *Some possible solutions for fraction puzzles*

Question 3 asks students to find another solution to this puzzle. Each group should try to find another solution. An additional solution is shown in Figure 21.

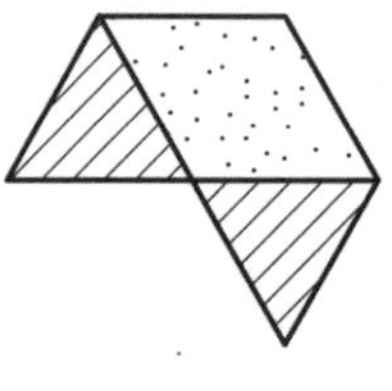

$\frac{2}{6} + \frac{1}{3} = \frac{2}{3}$

Figure 21: *Another possible puzzle solution for **Question 3** in the* Student Guide

Students are now ready to solve the first puzzle. Give each group a set of clues for Puzzle A. Each student should receive one clue. Remind students that they can only share their clues with other members of their group by reading the clue aloud.

Once a group has a solution that they feel satisfies all of the clues, they record their work by tracing the pattern blocks that they used onto a sheet of paper. They then write a number sentence to represent their solution. This allows you to check each group's solution at a later time.

Once a group completes a puzzle, you can either collect their clues and give them the clues for the next puzzle or ask them if they can solve the puzzle in another way. Each puzzle has multiple solutions. Accept any solution that fits all the puzzle clues. One possible solution for each is shown in Figure 22.

After a group has completed all three puzzles, they proceed to Part 2 of this lesson.

Part 2. Assessment Puzzle

Before students begin writing their solutions, discuss the Student Rubrics: *Solving* and *Telling* in order to make your expectations clear. Each student should receive one clue for the assessment puzzle (Puzzle D). Remind each student that he or she can only share his or her clue by reading it aloud to the group. Allow time for each group to find a solution to the puzzle.

After finding a solution that all members agree upon, students begin the second part of the assessment. This should be completed independently. Each student completes a copy of the *Puzzle Problem* Assessment Blackline Master, which asks students to describe the group's solution and explain the strategies used to solve the problem.

Suggestions for Teaching the Lesson

Homework and Practice

- Assign homework ***Questions 1–7*** on the *Fraction Puzzles* Activity Pages in the *Student Guide.* These questions review comparing and ordering fractions.
- DPP items S through V all build students' number sense. Bit S asks students to translate between word and symbolic representations of fractions. Challenge T reinforces the fraction concepts of this unit. Bit U addresses even numbers and multiples of 4. Challenge V poses an open-response question involving money.
- Home Practice Part 6 provides an arithmetic review and can provide practice for the Midterm Test in Lesson 9.

Answers for Part 6 of the Home Practice can be found in the Answer Key at the end of this lesson and at the end of this unit.

3. Write a number sentence for each pair of fractions. Use the symbols <, >, or = in each sentence.

   A. $\frac{6}{8}, \frac{3}{4}$ B. $\frac{3}{5}, \frac{3}{8}$ C. $\frac{1}{3}, \frac{3}{6}$

   D. $\frac{1}{2}, \frac{5}{10}$ E. $\frac{4}{5}, \frac{5}{12}$ F. $\frac{3}{9}, \frac{1}{3}$

4. Frank and Jerome each ordered a small cheese pizza for lunch. Frank's pizza was cut into 6 pieces. Jerome's pizza was cut into 8 pieces. Frank ate 2 pieces of his pizza. Jerome ate 3 pieces of his pizza. Which boy ate more pizza? How do you know?

5. Nila and Tanya shared a sandwich for lunch. Nila ate $\frac{1}{2}$ of the sandwich and Tanya ate $\frac{1}{4}$ of the sandwich. What fraction of the whole sandwich did the two girls eat? Explain how you found your answer.

6. Lee Yah, Luis, John, and Shannon solved a fraction puzzle. Their solution is found below. If a yellow hexagon is one whole, write a number sentence for their solution.

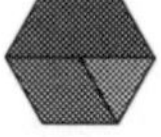

7. Frank, Jacob, Irma, and Maya solved a fraction puzzle. Their solution is shown on the right. Does their solution fit the clues? Explain your thinking.

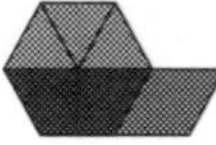

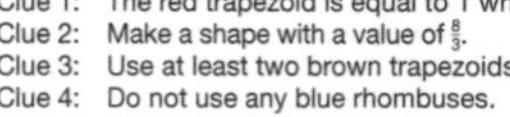

Clue 1: The red trapezoid is equal to 1 whole.
Clue 2: Make a shape with a value of $\frac{8}{3}$.
Clue 3: Use at least two brown trapezoids.
Clue 4: Do not use any blue rhombuses.

Fraction Puzzles SG · Grade 4 · Unit 12 · Lesson 8 355

***Student Guide* - Page 355**

Daily Practice and Problems: Challenges for Lesson 8

T. Challenge: Art Paper (URG p. 21) N

Carlos and Brandon each cut out a rectangle from a piece of drawing paper. Carlos's rectangle was larger—it was $\frac{1}{2}$ of his piece of paper. Brandon's was smaller, but it was $\frac{3}{4}$ of his whole piece.

1. Use *Centimeter Grid Paper* to draw a sketch of Brandon's and Carlos's whole pieces of paper.
2. Shade $\frac{1}{2}$ of Carlos's piece of paper.
3. Shade $\frac{3}{4}$ of Brandon's piece of paper.

V. Challenge: Bank Deposit (URG p. 22)

The bank gives Maya wrappers so she can roll the coins she saves. Then, she deposits the coins. The table shows the value of 1 roll of each type of coin.

Type of Coin	Value of 1 Roll
pennies	50¢
nickels	$2.00
dimes	$5.00
quarters	$10.00

Maya counts her change and puts the coins in wrappers. She has a total of $18.68. What types of coins could she have? How many full rolls of these coins could she have? How many coins would she have left over? List two possible combinations.

Name ______________________ Date ____________

Part 6 Arithmetic Review

1. Solve the following problems using mental math or paper and pencil. Estimate to make sure your answers are reasonable.

A. $231 \times 4 =$ B. $409 \times 5 =$ C. $6283 \times 4 =$ D. $570 \times 5 =$

E. $46 \times 92 =$ F. $27 \times 44 =$ G. $70 \times 40 =$ H. $83 \times 50 =$

I. $1092 + 378 =$ J. $3807 - 797 =$ K. $3450 + 4750 =$ L. $8367 - 538 =$

2. Explain your estimation strategy for Question 1C.

3. Solve the following problems.

A. John's uncle is taking a test to be a cashier at a grocery store. He must show all the ways to give 59¢ in change using exactly 10 coins. Show at least two ways to do this.

B. The questions on a math test are each worth a certain number of points. Use the table to find the total points if the four questions are answered correctly.

Question	Points Possible
A	$2\frac{1}{2}$
B	$3\frac{1}{4}$
C	5
D	$4\frac{1}{4}$

196 DAB · Grade 4 · Unit 12 EXPLORING FRACTIONS

***Discovery Assignment Book* - Page 196**

Assessment

- The *Puzzle Problem* can be scored using the Solving and Telling dimensions of the TIMS Multidimensional Rubric. To assist you in scoring students' work using these two dimensions, questions specific to this task follow:

  ### Solving

  Did students devise a good plan for solving the problem without assistance from the teacher?

  Did students organize their efforts for solving the problem?

  Did students stick with the problem until they found a solution that was acceptable to all group members?

  Did students look back at their clues and check their work for accuracy?

  ### Telling

  Did students clearly show their solution to this problem using pictures and symbols (a correct number sentence) to clarify their work?

  Did students include an explanation of their strategies that was complete and clear?

  Did students support their solution by referring back to the guidelines presented in the clues?

  Did students use appropriate fraction names in their explanation?

  After students have completed their written work, the teacher can review it and make comments. For example, if students do not use both a picture and a number sentence to show their solutions, suggest that they do so. Students should then revise their work based on teacher input. The work should be scored, and students should add the assessment to their collection folders.

- This activity provides an opportunity to assess students' abilities to solve open-response problems and communicate solution strategies. Record your observations on the *Observational Assessment Record.*
- Transfer appropriate documentation from the Unit 12 *Observational Assessment Record* to the students' *Individual Assessment Record Sheets.*

Extension

Ask groups to find at least two different solutions for each puzzle.

AT A GLANCE

Math Facts and Daily Practice and Problems

DPP Bit S reviews different representations of fractions. Challenge T provides practice with fraction concepts. Bit U reviews multiples and even numbers. Challenge V is a money problem.

Before the Activity

Prepare the clue cards for Fraction Puzzles A–D using the *Puzzle Clues* Blackline Masters.

Part 1. Fraction Puzzles

1. Review class rules for group work.
2. Read the vignette on the *Fraction Puzzles* Activity Pages in the *Student Guide.*
3. Ask students to evaluate the two puzzle solutions in the *Student Guide* ***(Questions 1–2)***.
4. Students work in groups to find additional solutions to the same puzzle ***(Question 3)***.
5. Students work in groups of four to solve the first three fraction puzzles (A–C). They record their solutions by drawing pictures and writing appropriate number sentences.

Part 2. Assessment Puzzle

1. Review the Student Rubrics: *Solving* and *Telling* with students.
2. Pass out a set of clues for Puzzle D to each group.
3. Groups work together to find a solution to the puzzle.
4. Each student works independently to write an explanation of his or her group's solution and a paragraph describing the problem-solving strategies used on the *Puzzle Problem* Assessment Blackline Master.
5. Students revise their work based on teacher feedback.
6. Score student work using the Solving and the Telling dimensions of the TIMS Multidimensional Rubric.
7. Students add their work to their collection folders.

Homework

1. Assign homework ***Questions 1–7*** in the *Student Guide.*
2. Assign Home Practice Part 6.

Assessment

1. Puzzle D and the *Puzzle Problem* Assessment Blackline Master provide an assessment of students' problem-solving and communication skills.
2. Use the *Observational Assessment Record* to note students' abilities to solve open-response problems and communicate solution strategies.
3. Transfer appropriate documentation from the Unit 12 *Observational Assessment Record* to the students' *Individual Assessment Record Sheets.*

Notes:

Name ________________________ Date ____________

Fraction Puzzle Clues

Each group will need one set of puzzle clues for each puzzle. Cut out puzzle clues for Puzzles A–D before class begins. Puzzle D is designed as an assessment and should be used after the other three puzzles have been successfully completed.

PUZZLE A	PUZZLE A
The yellow hexagon equals 1 whole.	Use 3 or more blocks to make your shape.
PUZZLE A	PUZZLE A
Use at least two different colors of blocks.	Make a shape with the value of $\frac{3}{4}$.

PUZZLE B	PUZZLE B
Make a shape with the value of $\frac{3}{2}$.	Use at least 1 blue rhombus.
PUZZLE B	PUZZLE B
The yellow hexagon equals 1 whole.	Use two brown trapezoids.

Name ______________________ Date ______________

PUZZLE C Use no more than 3 blocks.	PUZZLE C The red trapezoid equals 1 whole.
PUZZLE C Use at least two blocks.	PUZZLE C Make a shape with the value of $\frac{5}{3}$.

Assessment Puzzle Clues

PUZZLE D Make a shape with the value of $\frac{5}{6}$.	PUZZLE D The yellow hexagon equals 1 whole.
PUZZLE D Use 3 or 4 blocks.	PUZZLE D Use at least 1 green triangle, but not all green triangles.

Name ______________________ Date ______________

Puzzle Problem

Work together with your group. Use the four clues to help you build a shape using pattern blocks that meet all the guidelines.

1. Show your group's solution below. Draw a picture and write a number sentence.

2. Write a paragraph explaining the strategies your group used to arrive at this solution.

Student Guide

Questions 1–3 (SG p. 354)

1. *Solution satisfies all guidelines.
2. *Since the figure is made up of all green triangles, the solution does not satisfy the guideline that says, "Use at least 1 green triangle, but not all green triangles."
3. *Another possible solution: $\frac{2}{6} + \frac{1}{3} = \frac{2}{3}$

Homework (SG pp. 354–355)

Questions 1–7

1. A. $\frac{1}{9}, \frac{1}{8}, \frac{1}{5}, \frac{1}{3}$
   B. $\frac{3}{10}, \frac{3}{8}, \frac{3}{5}, \frac{3}{4}$
   C. $\frac{1}{2}, \frac{5}{8}, \frac{2}{3}, \frac{3}{4}$
   D. $\frac{1}{4}, \frac{3}{8}, \frac{2}{5}, \frac{5}{12}$
2. A. $\frac{1}{8}, \frac{1}{5}, \frac{1}{3}, \frac{1}{2}$
   B. $\frac{2}{10}, \frac{2}{6}, \frac{2}{5}, \frac{2}{4}$
   C. $\frac{4}{12}, \frac{4}{8}, \frac{4}{6}, \frac{4}{5}$
   D. $\frac{3}{10}, \frac{3}{8}, \frac{3}{5}, \frac{3}{4}$
   E. When the numerators are the same, the smaller fractions have the larger denominators.
3. A. $\frac{6}{8} = \frac{3}{4}$
   B. $\frac{3}{5} > \frac{3}{8}$
   C. $\frac{1}{3} < \frac{3}{6}$
   D. $\frac{1}{2} = \frac{5}{10}$
   E. $\frac{4}{5} > \frac{5}{12}$
   F. $\frac{3}{9} = \frac{1}{3}$
4. Jerome ate $\frac{3}{8}$ of his pizza. Frank ate $\frac{2}{6}$ of his pizza. Jerome ate more pizza than Frank. Students may use their fraction charts to compare $\frac{2}{6}$ and $\frac{3}{8}$.
5. $\frac{3}{4}$ of the sandwich; Strategies will vary.
6. $\frac{1}{2} + \frac{1}{6} + \frac{1}{3} = 1$
7. No, they used a blue rhombus.

Discovery Assignment Guide

**** Home Practice (p. 196)**

Part 6. Arithmetic Review

Questions 1–3

1. A. 924
   B. 2045
   C. 25,132
   D. 2850
   E. 4232
   F. 1188
   G. 2800
   H. 4150
   I. 1470
   J. 3010
   K. 8200
   L. 7829
2. Possible strategy: $6000 \times 4 = 24{,}000$
3. A. Answers will vary. Correct responses include:
   5 dimes + 1 nickel + 4 pennies;
   2 quarters + 9 pennies;
   1 quarter + 4 nickels + 1 dime + 4 pennies
   B. 15 points

Unit Resource Guide

Fraction Puzzle Clues (URG pp. 90–91)

*See Figure 22 in Lesson Guide 8 for answers to Puzzles A–C.

Puzzle Problem (URG p. 92)

Questions 1–2

1. Answers will vary. One possible solution to Puzzle D: $\frac{2}{3} + \frac{1}{6} = \frac{5}{6}$

2. *Answers will vary.

***Answers and/or discussion are included in the Lesson Guide.**
****Answers for all the Home Practice in the *Discovery Assignment Book* are at the end of the unit.**

Daily Practice and Problems: Bit for Lesson 9

W. Division Quiz: 9s (URG p. 23) 

A. 72 ÷ 9 = B. 63 ÷ 9 =

C. 54 ÷ 9 = D. 36 ÷ 9 =

E. 81 ÷ 9 = F. 45 ÷ 9 =

G. 9 ÷ 9 = H. 27 ÷ 9 =

I. 18 ÷ 9 =

The DPP Task is on page 95. Suggestions for using the DPPs are on page 95.

LESSON GUIDE 

Midterm Test

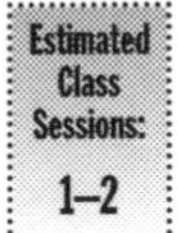

Students take a paper-and-pencil test consisting of items testing skills and concepts studied in Units 9, 10, 11, and 12.

Key Content

- Assessing concepts and skills.

Materials List

Print Materials for Students

		Math Facts and Daily Practice and Problems	Assessment Activity	Written Assessment
Student Book	Student Guide		Fraction Chart from *Comparing Fractions* Page 336	
Teacher Resources	Facts Resource Guide (CD)	DPP Item 12W		DPP Item 12W *Division Quiz: 9s*
	Unit Resource Guide	DPP Items W–X Page 23 (CD)		DPP Item W *Division Quiz: 9s* Page 23 and (CD) *Midterm Test* Pages 96–100, 1 per student

(CD) *available on Teacher Resource CD*

All Transparency Masters, Blackline Masters, and Assessment Blackline Masters in the Unit Resource Guide are on the Teacher Resource CD.

Supplies for Each Student

calculators
rulers
protractors
base-ten pieces
pattern blocks
fraction chart made in Lesson 3

Developing the Assessment

Students take this test individually. This test is designed to be completed in one or two class periods. However, you may want to allow more time. Part 1 assesses students' fluency with paper-and-pencil multiplication of one- and two-digit numbers and their estimation skills. Students are to complete this part of the test without a calculator. For Part 2, students will need a ruler, protractor, and a calculator. Base-ten pieces, students' fraction charts, and pattern blocks should also be available.

Remind students to read the directions carefully and to give full explanations of their problem-solving strategies when asked.

Suggestions for Teaching the Lesson

Homework and Practice

DPP Task X provides measurement practice that requires understanding of geometric concepts and terminology.

Assessment

- DPP Bit W is a quiz on division facts for the nines.
- The *Midterm Test* assesses skills and concepts studied in Units 9, 10, 11, and 12. Add this test to students' portfolios so you can compare students' performance on this test to their performance on similar activities throughout the year.

Daily Practice and Problems: Task for Lesson 9

X. Task: Drawing Line Segments 
(URG p. 23)

Draw a 5-cm segment on your paper and label the endpoints E and G. Measure and mark the midpoint with the letter F. Extend the line 2 cm past E and label the new endpoint D. Now measure the length of $\overline{DF}$.

AT A GLANCE

Math Facts and Daily Practice and Problems

DPP Bit W is a short quiz on division facts. DPP Task X provides practice with measuring.

Developing the Assessment

1. Students complete Part 1 of the test, ***Questions 1–9,*** without using a calculator.
2. Students complete Part 2 of the test, ***Questions 10–25,*** using classroom tools, including rulers, protractors, fraction charts, and pattern blocks.
3. Use DPP Bit W to assess students' fluency with the division facts for the nines.

Notes:

Name ______________________________ Date ______________

Midterm Test

Part 1

Use a paper-and-pencil method to complete each of the following problems. Use estimation to check to see if your answer is reasonable.

1. $\begin{array}{r} 73 \\ \times 8 \\ \hline \end{array}$

2. $\begin{array}{r} 28 \\ \times 23 \\ \hline \end{array}$

3. $\begin{array}{r} 56 \\ \times 44 \\ \hline \end{array}$

Use what you know about multiplying by tens to complete the following problems.

4. A. $40 \times 10 =$ __________
   B. $40 \times 100 =$ __________
   C. $40 \times 1000 =$ __________

5. A. $20 \times 20 =$ __________
   B. $20 \times 200 =$ __________
   C. $20 \times 2000 =$ __________

6. A. $50 \times 100 =$ __________
   B. $50 \times 200 =$ __________
   C. $50 \times 300 =$ __________

Estimate the answer to each of the following problems. Write a number sentence to show your thinking. Note: You do not need to find an exact answer.

7. 29×31

8. 48×19

9. 71×21

Name ______________________ Date ______________

Part 2

You may use any of the tools that you use in class to complete the remaining problems on this test. For example, you may use a ruler, a protractor, base-ten pieces, or a calculator.

Use the following figure to complete Questions 10–14.

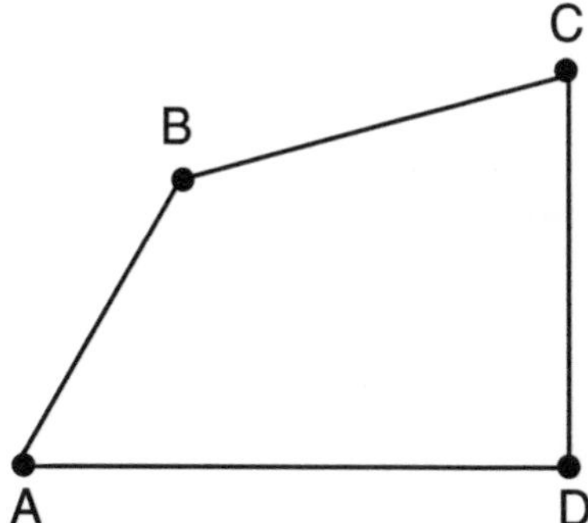

10. Find the measures of the angles.

∠A = ______________ ∠B = ______________

∠C = ______________ ∠D = ______________

11. Name the two rays that form angle C.

12. $\overline{AD}$ is part of what line?

13. **A.** Do any of the lines that form quadrilateral ABCD appear to be parallel?

B. If so, name the lines.

14. **A.** Do any of the lines that form quadrilateral ABCD appear to be perpendicular?

B. If so, name the lines.

Name ______________________________ Date ____________________

Use the following figure to complete Questions 15–16.

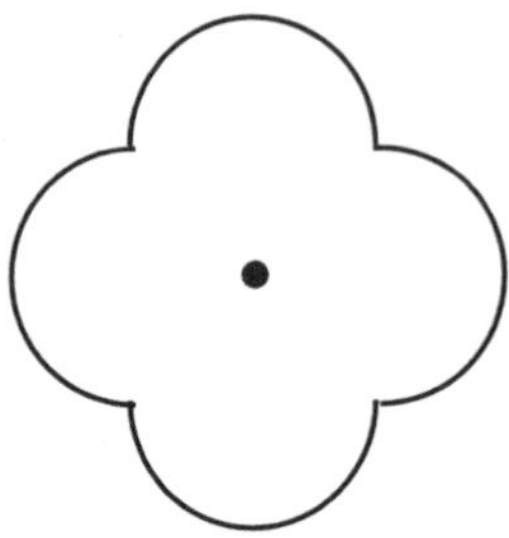

15. **A.** Does this figure have line symmetry?

    B. If so, sketch the lines of symmetry.

16. **A.** Does this figure have turn symmetry?

    B. If so, give the type of turn symmetry.

17. A flat in the base-ten pieces is equal to one whole.

    A. What is the value of a skinny?

    B. What is the value of a bit?

18. A flat in the base-ten pieces is equal to one whole. Write the following numbers using base-ten shorthand.

    A. 2.45 **B.** 17.26 **C.** 23.03

Name ______________________ Date ______________

19. A flat is equal to one whole. Write a decimal fraction and a common fraction for each of the following numbers.

Use the following graph to complete Question 20.

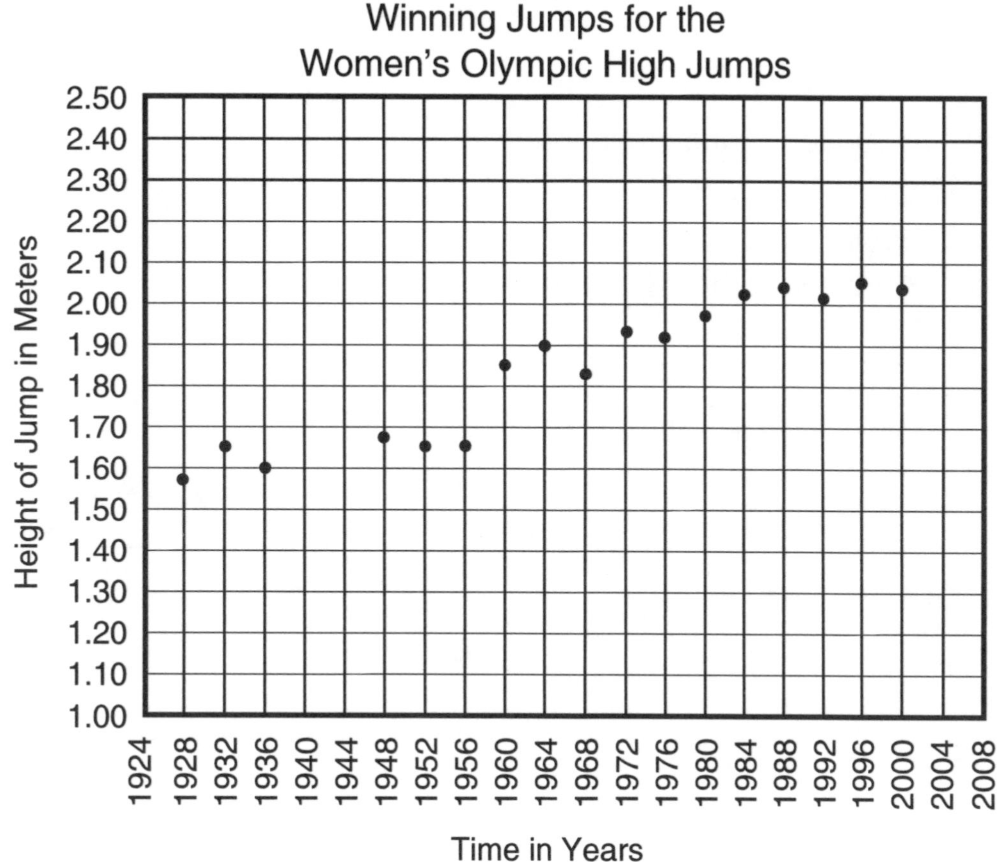

20. A. What was the height of the winning jump in 1960?

B. There were no Olympic Games in 1940 or 1944 during World War II. Predict the height of the winning jump if there had been a high jump contest in 1944.

C. Did you use interpolation or extrapolation to answer Question 20B? Explain.

Name ______________________ Date ______________

You may use your fraction chart or pattern blocks to help you answer Questions 21–25.

21. If the blue rhombus is one whole,

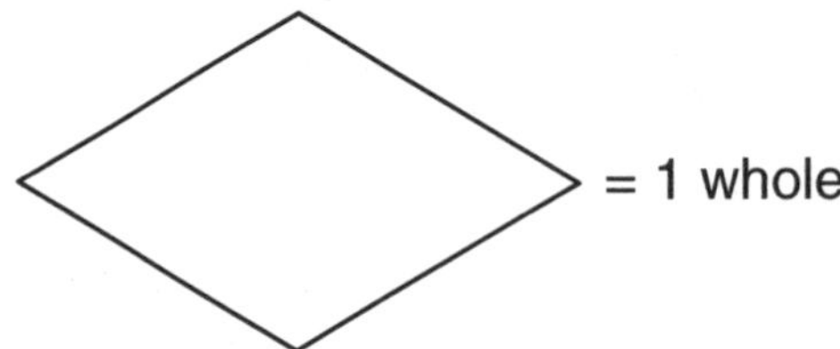

A. What fraction is one green triangle?

B. What fraction is three green triangles?

22. If the green triangle is $\frac{1}{3}$, draw one whole.

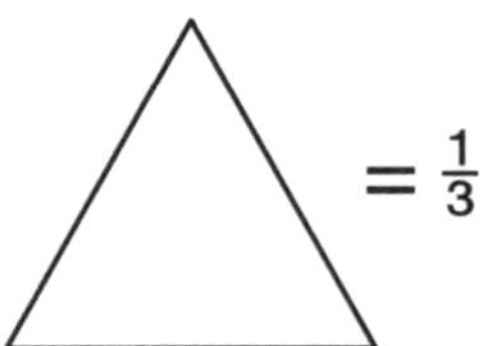

23. Put the following fractions in order from smallest to largest.

A. $\frac{3}{10}, \frac{3}{4}, \frac{3}{12}$

B. $\frac{1}{4}, \frac{5}{9}, \frac{1}{2}$

24. Complete the following number sentences.

A. $\frac{2}{3} = \frac{?}{12}$

B. $\frac{10}{12} = \frac{5}{?}$

C. $\frac{3}{5} = \frac{?}{15}$

25. Michael ate $\frac{3}{8}$ of his apple at lunch time. He ate $\frac{2}{8}$ of his apple after school.

A. How much of his apple did he eat?

B. How much of his apple is left?

Unit Resource Guide

Midterm Test (URG pp. 96–100)

Part 1

Questions 1–9

1. 584
2. 644
3. 2464
4. A. 400
   B. 4000
   C. 40,000
5. A. 400
   B. 4000
   C. 40,000
6. A. 5000
   B. 10,000
   C. 15,000

For Questions 7–9, estimates will vary. One possible estimate is shown.

7. $30 \times 30 = 900$
8. $50 \times 20 = 1000$
9. $70 \times 20 = 1400$

Part 2

Questions 10–25

10. $\angle A = 60°$, $\angle B = 135°$, $\angle C = 75°$, $\angle D = 90°$
11. $\overrightarrow{CB}$ and $\overrightarrow{CD}$
12. $\overleftrightarrow{AD}$
13. A. No.
14. A. Yes.
    B. $\overleftrightarrow{CD}$ and $\overleftrightarrow{AD}$
15. A. Yes.
    B.

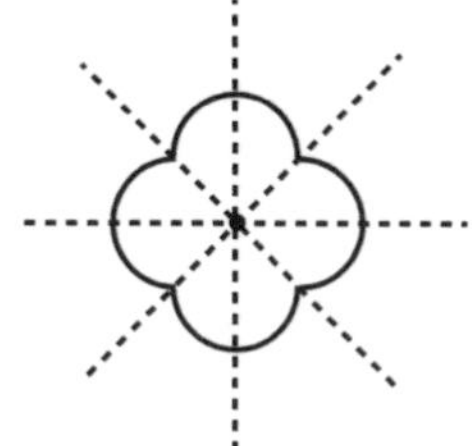

16. A. Yes
    B. $\frac{1}{4}$–turn symmetry
17. A. 0.1 or $\frac{1}{10}$
    B. 0.01 or $\frac{1}{100}$
18. A.
    B.
    C.
19. A. 1.35 and $1\frac{35}{100}$
    B. 12.08 and $12\frac{8}{100}$
    C. 20.4 and $20\frac{4}{10}$
20. A. 1.85 m
    B. Answers will vary. About 1.65 m
    C. Interpolation. Prediction is between data points.
21. A. $\frac{1}{2}$
    B. $\frac{3}{2}$ or $1\frac{1}{2}$
22.

Note: Arrangements of triangles may vary.

23. A. $\frac{3}{12}, \frac{3}{10}, \frac{3}{4}$
    B. $\frac{1}{4}, \frac{1}{2}, \frac{5}{9}$
24. A. $\frac{2}{3} = \frac{8}{12}$
    B. $\frac{10}{12} = \frac{5}{6}$
    C. $\frac{3}{5} = \frac{9}{15}$
25. A. $\frac{5}{8}$
    B. $\frac{3}{8}$

***Answers and/or discussion are included in the Lesson Guide.**
****Answers for all the Home Practice in the *Discovery Assignment Book* are at the end of the unit.**

Discovery Assignment Book

Home Practice

Part 2. Multiplication

Questions 1–2 (DAB p. 193)

1. A. 0
   B. 211
   C. 0
   D. 7898
   E. 8
   F. 17
   G. 9
   H. 6
   I. 20
   J. 140
2. 6, 12, 18, 24, 30, 36, 42, 48, 54, 60
   An even number has 2 as a factor. Since 2 is a factor of 6, 2 is a factor of all of the multiples of 6. So, all the multiples of 6 are even numbers.

Part 3. Fraction Chart

Questions 1–5 (DAB p. 194)

1. A. $\frac{2}{12}, \frac{1}{4}, \frac{3}{8}, \frac{2}{3}, \frac{5}{6}$
   B. $\frac{1}{10}, \frac{1}{8}, \frac{4}{9}, \frac{1}{2}, \frac{3}{5}$
2. Answers will vary. Students name 1 or 2 equivalent fractions for each letter.
   A. $\frac{3}{4}, \frac{9}{12}$
   B. $\frac{1}{3}, \frac{4}{12}$
   C. $\frac{4}{6}, \frac{6}{9}, \frac{8}{12}$
   D. $\frac{2}{5}$
   E. $\frac{6}{10}$
   F. $\frac{1}{4}, \frac{2}{8}$
   G. $\frac{1}{2}, \frac{2}{4}, \frac{3}{6}, \frac{4}{8}, \frac{5}{10}$
   H. $\frac{2}{10}$
3. A. $\frac{5}{6} = \frac{10}{12}$
   B. $\frac{8}{10} = \frac{4}{5}$
   C. $\frac{4}{5} = \frac{16}{20}$
4. Answers will vary.
5. Answers will vary.

Part 4. Fractions and Decimals (DAB p. 195)

Base-Ten Shorthand	Common Fraction	Decimal Fraction
\/·····	$\frac{25}{100}$ or $\frac{1}{4}$	0.25
□·	$1\frac{1}{100}$	1.01
···	$\frac{3}{100}$	0.03
□□□□□ /\/\\	$5\frac{5}{10}$ or $5\frac{1}{2}$	5.5
/\/	$\frac{3}{10}$	0.3
□□□□ //\·······	$4\frac{37}{100}$	4.37
□□····	$2\frac{4}{100}$	2.04
□□□□ /······	$4\frac{16}{100}$	4.16
□ \/\\·	$10\frac{41}{100}$	10.41

Part 5. A Fraction of a Meter

Questions 1–7 (DAB p. 195)

1. Answers will vary. Possible response: $\frac{6}{10}$ m
2. $\frac{7}{10}$ of a meter
3. Answers will vary. Possible responses: 25 cm or 0.25 m
4. Answers will vary. Possible response: $\frac{1}{10}$ m
5. Answers will vary. Possible response: $\frac{1}{2}$
6. Answers will vary. Possible responses: $1\frac{3}{4}$ or 1.75 meters
7. Answers will vary. Possible response: 2 meters

*Answers and/or discussion are included in the Lesson Guide.

Part 6. Arithmetic Review

Questions 1–3 (DAB p. 196)

1. A. 924
   B. 2045
   C. 25,132
   D. 2850
   E. 4232
   F. 1188
   G. 2800
   H. 4150
   I. 1470
   J. 3010
   K. 8200
   L. 7829
2. Possible strategy: $6000 \times 4 = 24{,}000$
3. A. Answers will vary. Correct responses include:
   5 dimes + 1 nickel + 4 pennies;
   2 quarters + 9 pennies;
   1 quarter + 4 nickels + 1 dime + 4 pennies
   B. 15 points

*Answers and/or discussion are included in the Lesson Guide.